Kick Heroin

Kick Heroin

Liz Cutland

Illustrated by Frances Broomfield

Sky Books, London

in association with

Gateway Books, Bath.

First published in 1985
by SKY BOOKS
188 Old Street, London EC1

in association with
GATEWAY BOOKS
19 Circus Place, Bath BA1 2PW

Set in Palacio 10½ on 12 by
MCS of Salisbury
Printed by Photobooks of Bristol
and bound by Ware of Clevedon

British Library Cataloguing in Publication Data

Cutland, Liz
Kick heroin.
1. Heroin habit——Great Britain
I. Title
361.2'93'0941 HV5822.H4

ISBN 0-946551-20-0

Contents

Acknowledgements

Writing this book was only possible with the sharing and support of a number of people. In 1975, I first visited the Hazelden Foundation in Minnesota, USA, where I started my training as a counsellor in the field of addiction. This continued at Meadowbrook, Minneapolis, under the guidance of Dr Jim Kincannon (now of the University of Minnesota). Since 1976, I have worked in the treatment team at Broadway Lodge at Weston-super-Mare and have continued to learn much about the disease of addiction and the recovery process. My colleagues past and present have taught me a great deal. However, my greatest insights into the effects of this illness came from the many addicts and their relatives with whom I have come into contact. This book is the outcome of their sharing part of their lives with me. For all this I am most grateful.

I would like to mention a number of specific people who have helped me get this book together: Barbara Mattick, who turned my scrawl into a neat typescript in her spare time; Brian Ballantyne who helped improve my knowledge of street language and who is mainly responsible for that part of the glossary; Geoff Evans, who shared his expertise as a pharmacist and counsellor; Bridie Dowse for her unfailing moral support; and William Pryor who originally suggested the idea of the book and has made it possible through his efforts in editing and publishing it.

All these people know, as I do, that recovery from addiction is possible. To them I would like to convey my gratitude for their encouragement and support in conveying this message.

I wish to thank the Hazledon Foundation of Centre City, Minnesota, for permission to quote from three of their pamphlets: *Free to Care* by Terrence Williams, *What is Spirituality*? by Paul Bjorklund, and *Perspectives on Treatment* by David Anderson.

Finally, I should point out that the addicts' and relatives' stories that I use are fictional – they do not describe any actual addicts or relatives but rather are compiled from my experience with all sorts of people.

Liz Cutland, *August 1985*

Foreword

In this book, Liz Cutland offers the public an opportunity to see how drug addiction, in particular that to heroin, should be considered a disease. She is plain and concise in her description of this dreadful addiction. She is balanced and caring in her view of both the addict and his relation to his family and the community. She makes no excuses for them and advises others against this form of escapism. At the end of the day, drug addicts, whether they take a prescribed drug, alcohol or street drugs, do it through their own choice. The affect of this decision is, however, the possible disintegration of the family and, more likely than anything, death.

It is this stark and final end product that makes Liz Cutland's book so important for those who have no knowledge of, but wish to learn about the impact of drug addiction and what can be done about it.

My hope is that this book will make clear that drug addiction or chemical dependency is a disease and that there is a future, that there can be recovery, and with the backing of AA, NA and FA both the addict and their families can live fruitful and happy lives.

Ann Parkinson (*wife of Cecil Parkinson M.P.*)

Introduction

Drug addiction, and in particular heroin addiction, is a very topical and much publicized subject, but, due to a lack of understanding and media hype, it is rarely seen in a practical light. In my opinion, this book is the first of its kind by a recognized expert to deal with the illness of addiction in a positive and realistic way.

I was a practising drug addict for five years and for three of those years my family and I sought help, exploring most of the other favoured methods of treatment – methadone, psychiatrists, the Paterson Black Box, periods in various institutions and long trips abroad. Amongst many things, I was treated for depression and neurosis and believed I had no hope of recovery. I ended up in a treatment centre run on the Minnesota Model and for the first time my family and I were given a seed of hope.

I was desperate, angry, terrified and totally out of touch with reality, but with the precious help of Liz Cutland and her colleagues I slowly learnt about my illness, myself and what I had to do to get better. I have now been totally free of drugs for four years; I attend self-help groups regularly and lead a normal and contented life with my husband and one-year-old daughter.

Liz Cutland dispels many of the myths surrounding heroin addiction and in treating it as a family illness offers help not only to the addict but to all those close to them. Using fictitious examples to aid identification she gives comfort and the realization that one is not alone in the frightening world of drugs. She does not glamourize, nor over-dramatize addiction and offers advice on both a practical and emotional level. The chapter on *Letting Go* is specially useful.

Kick Heroin is a must for anyone who comes into contact with drugs, and goes a long way to providing a much needed realistic, practical and informative survey of addiction.

Pandora Delevingne (*daughter of Jocelyn Stevens*)

1. Recovery is Possible

I hope this book will help many heroin addicts to kick their habit. I have assumed that the majority of those who have become addicted to heroin will not be interested in what these pages have to say while they are still addicted. People who are hooked on drugs are rarely aware of the seriousness of their problem and are wary of anything that might suggest the need to give them up. Usually addicts have to be coerced into getting help.

Instead, it is hoped that the following pages will be helpful to those relatives and friends of addicts who live with the constant fear, despair and anguish of having a loved one who is addicted to heroin. Many of the families with whom I have worked have been searching in vain for years for some way to stop their son, daughter, husband, wife, brother or sister from using heroin. A large number have given up hope. Some, as a last resort, have disowned their relative. Others have found themselves praying for the death of their addict because of a belief that this is the only way that the person can achieve peace of mind. In fact, several of the parents who have asked me for help have been advised by doctors, psychiatrists and social workers that addicts do not recover; that they all die as a result of their addiction.

For the past ten years I have worked with addicts and their families, both in this country and the United States. I consider myself lucky to have among my friends, people who 'kicked their habit' many years ago and who are living contented, fulfilling, drug-free lives. Those are the people who have taught me everything I know about addiction and its effects on addicts and their close friends and relatives. Even more important, they have demonstrated over and over again that recovery from addiction is possible.

Among these is Sarah who started using heroin at the age of sixteen. She came from a fairly poor background and in order to support her addiction she resorted to shoplifting, picking pockets, prostitution, and eventually, pushing drugs. I first met her nine years ago in an addiction treatment centre. She had just spent two years in prison for smuggling drugs into the country. At twenty-two, she had had several jobs but had never held them down for more than a month. She had contracted hepatitis from using dirty needles and had overdosed three times. She was aggressive, suspicious, full of guilt and extremely manipulative. Her family did not want to know her. Sarah fought the treatment programme all the way. She denied that addiction was her problem. She saw herself as the victim of a cruel misunderstanding world. She did not want to give up drugs as she believed that they were her only pleasure in life. The staff at the centre were on the point of discharging her for not co-operating with treatment, when an ex-boyfriend died from an overdose of heroin. Sarah was very upset; suddenly, she changed. She started to attempt most of the therapeutic tasks she was asked to do and eventually completed treatment.

Recently I heard from her. She has not touched drugs for nine years, with the aid and support of a self-help group which she still attends regularly. She is happily married with two children. Six months ago she started training as a counsellor in a drug addiction centre. After she had been off drugs for four years, she contacted her mother and they now have a close relationship. Mother looks after the children while Sarah is involved in her training programme. The reason that Sarah wrote to me was to let me know that she was very content with her life.

Another example is John, whose addiction did not become apparent for a very long time because he is very wealthy. Until his parents realized what was happening and started to try to control his purse strings he did not have to resort to the extremely devious behaviour in which Sarah had become involved. He was twenty-seven when he ended up in a treatment centre. Two years before his admission, he had held down a fairly responsible job in the Foreign Office from which he resigned because his obsession with heroin meant that he was spending less and less time in the office. He was arriving late and leaving early in order to 'score'. His concentration had become very sketchy.

After his resignation his parents tried to help by finding him work (for which he rarely bothered to turn up), by sending him to expensive nursing homes, controlling his trust fund, sending him on holiday to the South of France (where he continued to use), and by introducing him to 'nice' friends. The more they tried to help, the more John progressed into his illness and the more devious he became. He lied about his continual use of drugs; he stole money and jewellery from his mother to pay for them. He shut himself in his room and refused to communicate with anyone. Eventually, in desperation, his parents sent him to a treatment centre where a daughter of friends had received some help. He ran away from there after two weeks, not wanting to believe that he was an addict. He rationalized that since he smoked the heroin he was not hooked. He believed (wrongly) that to be a real addict you had to inject the heroin. He went to live with a girlfriend who also abused drugs.

Six months later John asked to be re-admitted to treatment. His girlfriend had left him, his parents did not want any contact with him while he was using drugs and he was sick and tired of being sick and tired. His dealers were also getting somewhat aggressive because he owed them a great deal of money.

This time John completed treatment, but he used heroin for a brief period shortly after. Fortunately, he received a lot of help from friends who are recovering addicts. He is now thirty years old and has not used drugs for two years. A year ago he started his own business, living on his own and keeping in regular contact with his parents. The trust between them is growing, slowly.

These are two of many success stories. It would be unrealistic to believe that recovery happens for every addicted person. Sadly, numbers of young people suffer horrible deaths as a result of hepatitis contracted from unhygienic needles, overdosing, or suicide. I believe that many of these deaths need not have happened but, unfortunately, there is a great deal of ignorance and blindness in our society about addiction and how to help those who have become slaves to heroin. Over the years, many myths have developed around the use of heroin – I hope the following chapters will dispel a number of these.

It is important to clarify what is meant in this book by 'recovery' from addiction. It is the achievement of living a full, contented and responsible life-style, while being totally abstinent from all mood-altering drugs; these include heroin, marijuana and alcohol, also prescribed drugs like methadone, valium and the other tranquillisers. I believe that this is possible for the large majority of addicts – if they are lucky enough to receive the right help. Other technical and slang expressions the reader might not be familiar with are also explained in the glossary at the end of the book.

One of the questions I am constantly being asked by relatives is "Where do I get help for my addict?". For this reason, I have compiled a brief directory of helping agencies at the end of this book. At present, they are few and far between; most are private clinics and most are in the south of England. Unfortunately, at this time, our Government, although doing some commendable and necessary work in trying to control the trafficking of drugs, is minimizing the extent of the existing problem of addiction. Despite the fact that the media give heroin addiction a lot of publicity and use the word 'epidemic' constantly, professional help in the addiction field only touches the tip of this particular iceberg. There is talk of Government money being made available to set up treatment programmes for addicts. Where are they?

Also, in my opinion, there are a number of well-meaning people in the 'helping' professions who try to help, but have never learned to understand addiction. Doctors who substitute one drug with another; psychiatrists who see addiction as a symptom of some deep underlying emotional problem, instead of seeing it as an illness in its own right; social workers and probation officers who fall into the trap of feeling over-responsible for their clients and, unknowingly, encourage the continuation of using by protecting the addicts from facing the consequences of their addictive behaviour.

The image of an addict does not encourage people to help him get well. He carries a very real stigma and, as a result, is often written off as a hopeless case. As members of society, we have our pre-conceptions and we rarely question them. The common stereotype of an addict is of someone who has no moral backbone, who has decided that he is above the law, has a death wish, is unable to cope with stress and who is highly irresponsible. We pass moral judgements and eventually choose to disassociate ourselves from that individual because we do not know how to respond.

Frequently, the addict's behaviour encourages this process of moralizing and stigmatizing. The purchase of heroin is illegal and he may break the law in other ways to get the money to buy the stuff. His behaviour under the influence of drugs can be embarrassing, worrying and extreme. Mood-altering chemicals lower his inhibitions; also, he often fails to meet his own expectations and those of others. He breaks promises, forgets about appointments; his work is sporadic; he is not dependable. When people who believe that addiction is only a weakness try to reason with him, he continues to use drugs. In short, addicts do not endear themselves to busy, but caring people, who might want to help. It is a fact that their heroin-induced behaviour often sets addicts up to be rejected.

The British culture encourages us to believe that families should be very self-sufficient and private. We are expected to cope with our problems within those units. Only in very extreme circumstances do we believe in washing our dirty linen in public or asking for outside help. There is the fear that whenever a serious problem is revealed that appears to have moral connotations, outsiders will point the finger and apportion blame. As a result, relatives will attempt to hide the addiction from the outside world, vainly trying to put the addict right themselves. This conspiracy of silence unwittingly encourages the progression of the addiction.

Narcotics Anonymous is a self-help group which has grown rapidly in the United Kingdom in the last four years and now has a membership of several hundreds. It has helped addicts achieve what most family members and professionals have failed to do. It is full of young people who are proving that it is possible to 'kick the habit'! Very often, this happens in spite of lack of understanding and support in the community. So many more people could have the opportunity to become well if only society opened its eyes, overcame its apathy and was prepared to *learn* about heroin addiction and the great possibility of recovery. (*see note p. 101*)

2. It is Not a Habit – It is an Addiction

Fred is twenty-one. He has been using heroin for two years and is very frightened of what it is doing to him. He has tried several times to give it up. Fred has a good brain. He did extremely well at school and his parents and teachers expected him to go on to a brilliant career. However, Fred has been asked to leave university. Before going to university he had smoked pot occasionally. Then he became involved with a group of friends who used and who introduced him to heroin. Fred loved the feeling he got from the drug. However, his concentration on his studies suffered and for two years he had bad grades. Before he was asked to leave, he stopped taking drugs for a period of six months and put a lot of effort into catching up with his work. At a friend's twenty-first birthday party he drank alcohol heavily and found himself using the syringe again. Three weeks later he was admitted to hospital in a coma, having overdosed. Fred was frightened, but when he was discharged from hospital, drove straight round to his dealers to score again. He said that he could not give up the habit.

ADDICTION – WHAT IS IT?

I dislike the use of the word 'habit' in the context of drug addiction. I use it here because it is part of the street jargon. However, I think it trivialises the seriousness of the problem. According to my dictionary the word means "ordinary course of behaviour, tendency to perform certain actions, custom, accustomedness". This suggests to me that it is a behaviour that could be controlled or fairly easily be given up, like going to bed at a certain time, or spending every Sunday morning reading the newspapers. To my mind the definition of the word 'disease' in the same dictionary gives a more accurate description. It means "disorder or want of health in mind or body; ailment; cause of pain".

Heroin addiction cannot be controlled or easily given up. The heroin is the master. It is the centre of the universe of those who are addicted to it. The feeling that an addict gets from heroin has often been compared to being in love. It is a total obsession. Everything else and everyone else is secondary to that drug and the feelings it produces; the urge to use is greater than the urge to eat, the sexual urge, or even the urge for survival.

An addict is a person who continues to use drugs, despite the fact that any, or all, of the following are suffering: health, family relationships, finances or effectiveness at work. A heroin addict is physically, emotionally and spiritually dependent on the drug. Although most addicts will use heroin to feel normal, they will also undergo a personality change in the process of the addiction. They may become self-centred, insensitive to others, devious, irresponsible, apathetic, manipulative and dishonest. Once the drug is in their system, users are powerless over their behaviour and they cannot predict what the outcome is going to be. The drug is in charge.

I have worked with addicts for ten years – fairly successfully, I believe. I still do not know what causes one person who tries heroin to become an addict and another to be indifferent to its effect. It is a myth that everyone who uses heroin automatically becomes addicted; some do, but some can take it and leave it. I do not believe that anyone has produced the answer as to why addiction happens for one and not for another. There is strong evidence to suggest that there is a genetic predisposition in many addicts which causes different biochemical reactions in the brain. However, this research is not conclusive. I will leave those who specialise in research and prevention to answer the question why. My interest is in helping those who already have the problem. As a disciple of Reality Therapy, I am not convinced that their knowing why will stop established addicts from using drugs. Numbers of relatives and friends have spent years agonizing over this question and much valuable time is wasted in trying to discover whose fault it is. Often the addict is blamed for being weak or easily led, the parents for being ineffectual or too strict, the educational and legal systems for being too lax, and friends for leading the addict astray. None of this helps the addict to get well; in fact, it provides all sorts of excuses for continuing to use.

It took me at least a year of intensive involvement and training in the addiction field to believe that what I was working with was an illness in its own right. My previous training had taught me to look into underlying motives. I had viewed addicts as weak-willed and immoral people who just needed to 'pull themselves together and get responsible'. I saw addiction as self-inflicted and was very sceptical of my colleagues who held the view that addicts were not responsible for having the disease of addiction, but having sought help, they were now responsible for maintaining their recovery. What finally convinced me to believe in the disease concept of addiction was seeing people who understood it as an illness make miraculous recoveries. I met many young people who had been written off as hopeless cases or had given up as almost dead, who were alive, healthy, totally drug-free and had a quality of life that I admired.

PHYSICAL ADDICTION

Looking back, I remember accepting the physical side of the addiction quite easily. I still do not understand why people sniff powder up their noses or go through the intricate ritual of chasing the dragon or, even, having a phobia about them, stick needles into their veins. I could see, however, that having pumped enough of the drug into their systems, the body suffered if it was denied that intoxicating substance. I saw people enduring the discomfort of withdrawal and the craving for more heroin. I observed the fear, sleeplessness, irritability, lack of concentration, muscular pain, abdominal cramps, dilated pupils, sweating, vomiting and lack of appetite, and I could understand the need for more of the drug to make the discomfort go away.

I had thought that withdrawal would be dramatic, only having the vivid images beloved of the cinema and mass media to go by. I have witnessed much more horrific withdrawal symptoms from alcohol and the heavy use of prescribed drugs such as valium and the other benzodiazepines. My medical colleagues tell me that generally it is much easier to withdraw heroin abusers from their chosen drug than it is to detoxify alcoholics or those who have abused tranquillisers. I mention this because I believe that many addicts and their relatives have been persuaded that it would be easier for the addict to stay on a controlled amount of heroin or to change to another addictive drug called methadone, rather than risk withdrawal. I am not advocating that anyone should try to 'cold turkey' and wean themselves off the drug. However, addicts can be withdrawn relatively easily, painlessly and quickly under medical supervision. For this purpose some doctors do use methadone in diminishing doses for a brief period. However it is not necessary to continue using methadone for prolonged periods of time; that is just substituting one addiction for another.

The first heroin addict I worked with when I was a trainee counsellor was a surprise to me because he was not being treated for heroin dependence, but for alcoholism. Mark had returned to the United States from Vietnam some time before I met him. On his return he had participated in a treatment programme for heroin addiction and had not used any street drugs since. Although he and his ex-wife swore that he had no problem with alcohol previous to his return to the States, he was diagnosed as a chronic alcoholic three years later.

This pattern of moving from one addiction to another has repeated itself in many heroin addicts. Others, when they have been unable to obtain the drug of their choice, have substituted alchohol or other drugs such as valium, cocaine or amphetamines. Some addicts start their dependence on alcohol and marijuana, gradually moving on to heroin. For the majority of addicts, once they have become dependent on one mood-altering chemical, it appears that they are potentially addicted to all such drugs, whether they have used them or not.

There is no known cure for addiction. I use the word 'recovery', I mean an arresting of the disease, not a permanent cure. Once human beings are dependent on heroin, then they are addicted for the rest of their lives. This does not mean that they have to use drugs for all of that time. But, if they do, they will not be able to control their use even after a long period of abstinence. I cannot stress strongly enough that recovery demands total abstinence from ALL mood-altering chemicals, prescribed or otherwise. Some addicts convince themselves that they can cope with smoking the odd joint of marijuana or having the occasional drink of alcohol. Usually, in time, this leads them right back to being dependent on heroin.

Several professional people who have a different understanding of addiction from mine, have regarded me in horror when I have mentioned that my colleagues and I recommend total abstinence from all mood-altering chemicals. We have been accused of taking the choice away from the individual. In fact, all of our patients do have the right to choose. However, the alternatives are very clear in my mind as a) total abstinence and recovery, or b) using drugs with the eventual loss of control and the probability of death. If someone is diagnosed as diabetic, we do not quibble if it is recommended that he gives up sugar. If cigarettes are ruining another's health, we question not the doctor's sanity if he suggests cutting out smoking altogether. Yet, well qualified people assume the right to advise addicts that it is perfectly acceptable to use mood-altering chemicals, whether the occasional glass of wine or a regular script of methadone. Such attitudes are justified by statements like "You cannot expect people to change too much; they need a crutch of some kind". It is easier for a heavy smoker to give up tobacco completely than to try to limit his cigarettes to five a day. When doctors recommend to addicts that they should control the use of mood altering substances, they are expecting the impossible; they are ignoring the meaning of the word addiction. An addict is a slave to any chemical which changes his mood. The only way to find freedom is totally to abolish such substances from his life.

EMOTIONAL AND SPIRITUAL DISEASE

As a non-addicted person, I had great difficulty in coming to terms with the emotional and spiritual side of dependence. I expected people who had 'got off' the drug physically, to stay off. Like Fred, whom I mentioned at the beginning of this chapter, many young people kicked the habit for a period of time but, despite the feelings of guilt and low self-esteem, despite almost being at death's door and the knowledge that they might hurt themselves and other people, they used again. Having used again, they climbed back on the painful roundabout of lies, deceit, theft, hurting others, fear of not being able to maintain their habit, of being caught, and persistent feelings of guilt; this was followed by using drugs again to anaesthetize the emotional pain and escape from reality.

In the early days of my involvement with the treatment of addiction, I did not appreciate the necessity to help patients recognize that they needed to change their life-style or find an alternative way of life which had as much, if not more, importance than heroin. It did not take me long to discover that the majority of addicts are not weak-willed as I believed. Once they have made the choice to abstain from drugs (including alcohol), have been given some help in coming to terms with the addiction and themselves and have changed the focus of their lives to something more positive, they frequently show remarkable determination and strength of character.

It is not easy recovering from an addiction. In fact, it is extremely hard work, but it is possible with the support of self-help groups. Recovery from other major illnesses like cancer, is not considered a matter of 'just exerting willpower', yet society, in its ignorance, demands this of those suffering the killing addictive diseases.

DENIAL

Everyone is aware that adolescence and early adulthood is a time of exploration of who we are as individuals, of discovering and establishing our beliefs and value systems. During this process, many experiment with nicotine, alcohol, sexual preferences, marijuana, and political stances of which the establishment disapproves. Some go on to experiment with hard drugs. Most people who do this do not believe that they will become addicted. Many of those who have been using drugs for years, continue to deny their dependence. Denial is an integral part of addiction.

So many parents and partners have complained bitterly about the dishonesty and blatant lying of their addict. It is seen as a deliberate and personal slight. Many people believe 'if he loved me, I would not be treated like this'. *Some* of this dishonesty is part of the denial system of the illness.

I was recently involved in a car accident. It was not serious, but my first reaction was to deny that it had happened; I just did not want to cope with the reality of the situation. A few weeks ago a friend of mine was told that her husband had cancer. He has accepted and come to terms with the situation, but she does not want to talk about it and will avoid anything which will bring to the fore what is actually happening. Many of us cling on to our delusions because we believe that they are less painful than reality. It is the same for addicts. An addict is a person who is dealing with conflict; on the one hand reality is relentlessly trying to impose awareness of impaired relationships, and on the other, heroin has become extremely important because it produces unusually good feelings and helps shut off bad feelings. At this point, there are only two possible resolutions of the conflict: reject using drugs, or reject reality. The fear of coping with life without heroin can be tremendous so most addicts are going to opt for rejecting reality until the use of drugs becomes too uncomfortable or too painful. When this occurs, many addicts will seek help. Relatives and friends can speed up this process by changing their attitude and by not cushioning the addict from the consequences of his drug abuse.

3. It is Much More than a Habit – It is a Family Addiction

For every addict, there are about three other people who endure the pain and chaos that ripples out from addiction. Most of us are brought up to believe that if we care about someone, we try to help that person. Often that belief is interpreted and acted on by absorbing or stopping some of the pain that the loved one is suffering. Unfortunately, through ignorance as well as best intentions, we help the addict to progress further into the illness by protecting him, thus preventing that person from facing the reality of his addiction.

The majority of human beings, whether they are addicted or not, need a family or a similar group of people as an emotional support system. Addicted people need families or friends in a special way. Without that protective support system they would not be able to continue with their drug use and survive. When we lie, cover up, pamper, pay debts, pretend nothing traumatic has happened, we do it because we care for the addicted person and because we do not wish that person to be upset. We do not want to rock the boat in case it provokes the use of more drugs. Unknowingly, what we are doing is allowing the addict to continue behaving in an irresponsible way and endorsing what his denial system is already telling him – that the situation is not that bad.

Many parents, partners, and sometimes children, believe that it is their duty to try to control the addict, and to try to stop the use of drugs. This results in those involved in close relationships becoming as obsessed with, or as addicted to, the addict as he is to heroin.

When those who have concern for the addict become hooked on him, they unwittingly enable him to progress further into the illness by becoming his caretaker. This can take several forms. Some take on the role of saviour; because these people are kind and loving, they believe that they have the responsibility to save the addict: ("I will do everything I can to sort him out. I am a capable person. Just give me time to find the answers").

Others become partners and may use drugs with the addict: ("If I join him perhaps I can learn to understand him better and we will become closer"). Some will become bullies, trying vainly to force the addict into changing his behaviour: ("What this kid needs is some tough discipline!")

Others assume the role of victim, or doormat, believing it is their mission in life to suffer: ("I know she has stolen from me, but, she is my daughter. Whatever she has done I will stand by her"). Those concerned with the addict will play one or more of these roles at one time or another. In so doing, they enter into a game with the addict by establishing themselves as being responsible for his behaviour.

One of the largest shocks I had in my training as a counsellor came from the fact that I was expected to be involved in the treatment programme as a patient! (There were three reasons for this – to learn about addiction and addictive thinking; to experience the treatment programme at first hand; and to look at myself and the way in which I related to addicts.) I was the only non-addicted person in a group of twenty-two women. For the first few days I stayed outside the group and took the role of observer. However, my fellow-patients would not tolerate this for long. It took little time for me to realize that the *only* difference between myself and the other women was that I had not abused addictive chemicals. I could identify with many of the feelings, attitudes and behaviours which were discussed in the group. For example, repressed anger, being manipulative and controlling, unrealistically high expectations of myself and others and, at that time, a feeling of low self-esteem. Some addicts may wish to be seen as special and different or as extraordinarily sensitive. They may even believe this but psychological tests show that, when off drugs for a period of time, their personalities are very similar to those of most cross-sections of society.

HOW ADDICTS AND THOSE INVOLVED BEHAVE

As I became more involved in working with people who were very close to those suffering from the illness, I found many similarities between the addicted persons and their relatives. In coping with the tension and confusion which surrounds the illness, many of the friends and relatives experienced similar feelings and behaviour to the addict. In some cases, family members can let their preoccupation with the addict destroy their lives and cause pain to others.

Denial

I have already discussed the denial practised by addicts and how relatives can become very upset by the behaviour. However, many of those in a close relationship with an addict can adopt a denial system too. It is part of the 'It could never happen in our family' syndrome. To some families the stigma of being labelled an addict is so horrifying that they prefer a diagnosis of schizophrenia or manic-depression. Somehow these labels are seen as more socially acceptable and yet those suffering from heroin addiction often have a better chance of recovery than those who have been afflicted with a psychiatric illness.

To the outside world, many relatives will act as though everything in life is wonderful. They will cope with the pain and trauma by putting up a brave front. Inside, they are being torn apart with the agony of shame, despair, fear, and feelings of impotence. Even to themselves they may minimize the extent of the problem. Often my colleagues and I heard horrific tales of the addict abusing his family when under the influence of drugs; yet, when we meet the relatives we are assured, because of misplaced loyalty, that 'things are not that bad really', or 'I don't think he has become addicted, yet'.

The No-Talking Rule

Most addicted people will avoid talking honestly about their drug use. If they do discuss it, it is usually greatly minimized.

To bring what is actually happening out into the open would mean confronting reality, and that may mean having to give up the substance which they love. Many addicts become extremely adroit at avoiding or changing the subject. They can also make it very uncomfortable for anyone who tries to talk about the addiction, by intimidation or by provoking feelings of guilt. A chemically dependent person can become very skilled at manipulating others into feeling guilty. Nothing needs to be said – it can be done with an injured look or by behaving so well for several weeks, that you wonder why you ever suspected he might have resumed using heroin. After all, he had given his word! He had promised to be strong and never be tempted by that drug again!

As a result, many family members find themselves avoiding talking about the drug-taking and subsequent behaviour because it may rock the boat and cause upset. The fear is that if addicts suffer from any distress, then they will use drugs to cope with these feelings. Actually, no-one makes an addict take heroin – we do not have that power. He uses because he feels like it. If he hasn't an obvious excuse, he will invent a variety of reasons. He will use if he is happy, sad, angry, or indifferent to what is going on around him. Not talking cushions the addict from facing reality. Not only do relatives not talk to him about the heroin use, but they often do not talk to each other about it either. In-depth sharing of thoughts and feelings is usually neglected in families where there is a person abusing drugs. Addiction can cause a 'dis-ease' of communication within a group of caring individuals.

Blaming

Partly because people do not understand or accept the disease concept and partly because of the denial surrounding the illness, the drug use has to be blamed on something or someone. Heroin addiction has to be seen as someone's fault. Many chemically dependent people see themselves as victims of others' behaviour. Parents may be blamed for being too strict, spouses and lovers will be charged with not making the effort to understand. Stress at work or boredom due to unemployment are other alibis often used. As long as an addict is using a scapegoat, he will not be taking responsibility for his recovery and, as a result, will not get well.

Unfortunately, many relatives fall into the same trap of blaming. Very often, the addict, who is trying to take the focus off himself, will use the situation to his advantage and play one family member off against another. For example, mother may be told her son is using drugs because he is unhappy in his marriage; he says his wife nags him continually and is more interested in her work than she is in him. To his wife he complains bitterly about his domineering mother who never made any effort to understand him as a child and sent him away to school at the first opportunity. The result is more pain and tension in the family because the two women are blaming each other for the addiction. Another example might be the family where mother and father are not communicating and are trying to cope with their daughter's addiction in different ways. Father plays the heavy hand and mother is protective, covering up a lot of the addictive behaviour. The daughter manipulates the situation and plays one off against the other. If she does not get want she wants from father, she will run to mother and the rift between her parents grows larger as they become more angry and continually blame each other. In so doing, the familiy is avoiding coming together and addressing the most important issue of how to help the addict recover from a killer disease.

Obsession

All heroin addicts are obsessed with their drug of choice. Someone who has just started using heroin may still be thinking 'How will my drug-taking affect my activities?' Often, by the time an addict receives help, the thinking has completely switched around to, 'How will my activities affect my use of heroin?' Everything in an addict's life is arranged around the use of heroin. Any person or situation that will get in the way of his desire to use heroin will either be ruthlessly dismissed or manipulated around.

The obsession of family members for the addict is parallel to his obsession for heroin. Relatives often arrange their lives around the addict. For instance, family holidays may be cancelled because he is using again. As a result, the other children in the family may feel and believe that they are of secondary importance. Friends may be contacted and asked to keep an eye open for any sign of drug use. Attitudes swing from asking 'How do we make life easier for him?' to trying aggressively to control him. Worry takes over the family; worrying about overdosing, about driving whilst under the influence of drugs, about being caught by the police and about what to expect next. Relatives may become so tense, fearful and angry that they begin to question their own sanity.

Being Protective.

Someone who is dependent on heroin will go to any lengths to protect the source of his supply. In fact, most addicts will have more than one source just in case the first one dries up. Heroin is the most important thing in their lives and in order to keep the supply coming they may go to any lengths; for example, they may lie, cover-up, steal from loved ones, resort to blackmail, prostitute themselves or become involved in dealing in drugs.

Close friends and relatives can be just as fiercely protective of their addict. I have worked with desperate wives who have stolen drugs in order to keep the peace and also to have money for food for the children. At some time, most relatives have lied to protect their addict, whether it be to the police, employer, another relative or friends outside the family. This is done with the best of intentions to stop the addict from getting hurt. What it does in fact is to make the addiction more comfortable for him and thus eases him further into the illness.

Not Accepting Loss of Control

The greatest obstacle for the addict struggling with recovery is the fact that he is not in control of the drug – heroin is in control of him. In my experience, one of the main purposes of treatment programmes is to help the addict break down his denial system and recognize that he is powerless over mood-altering chemicals. Often this takes weeks of group therapy, one-to-one counselling, and assignments where he describes (in writing or by the spoken word) specific situations where heroin or other drugs have taken control of his life.

Likewise, the most difficult problem for relatives and friends to come to terms with is that they have absolutely no control over the addict. Many believe that they should be able to exercise some control over him. Some see themselves as failures because they have not been able to stop the dependence on heroin.

Relatives may resort to extreme measures to try to prevent the use of drugs. Addicts have been locked in rooms, committed to psychiatric institutions, put in the charge of private nurses, beaten, deprived of all their money, sent abroad, enlisted in the armed forces, given drugs in controlled amounts, and bribed or thrown out of their homes. The more relatives and friends try to force the addict to give up heroin or maintain some controlled use of the substance, the more he continues to abuse the drug and the more inadequate and frustrated family members feel. Everyone in the family has become involved in a game where no-one wins, prolonging the belief that 'next time it will be different'.

Again, as long as an addict has someone in his life who accepts the responsibility for controlling the addiction, he is shielded from the reality of the situation. It is all too easy in these circumstances for him to continue seeing himself as a victim, when he will use drugs as a result of the subsequent feelings of self-pity and resentment. What better excuse than the high-handed behaviour of angry relatives?

Change of Personality

Often comments are made by relatives about dramatic changes in the addict's personality. Bright young people are transformed into 'zombies'. Once charming and considerate, they become aggressive, self-centred and sullen. Direct and honest men and women become deceitful and manipulative.

The illness of addiction can bring about changes in the personalities of members of the addict's family as well. People who prided themselves on being loving, tolerant and patient, suddenly find themselves becoming aggressive and bitter as they struggle to cope with the addiction. Many parents and spouses of addicts have coped with difficult problems in life, yet living with the addiction has left them depressed, disorganized and disorientated.

Isolation

Several of the patients I have seen in treatment for their addiction are extremely isolated from other people and consequently very lonely. Physically, they may have a number of people close to them but, emotionally, they are distanced from others. Heroin has anaesthetized their feelings so it is impossible to have a close, equally sharing relationship with anyone. By the time someone seeks treatment, any surviving friendships are usually with those who experience drugs in a similar way. An odd kind of comfort comes from supporting each other's denial system. In all likelihood, non-addicted people have either moved away or have been rejected by the addict. Non-using friends make addicts feel uneasy – they reveal the abnormality of the drug use.

A number of the relatives with whom I work have also become extremely isolated from others. Living with an addicted person can be a very lonely existence. Many close relatives believe that no-one else would understand, no other family has been through this pain and conflict. As a result of these feelings of alienation, of low self-esteem, of the obsession with and the need to control the addicted person, as well as the lack of communication and bitterness in the family, many relatives of addicts shut themselves off from other people.

HOW ADDICTS AND THOSE INVOLVED FEEL

As well as behaving in the same way as their addict, many relatives and friends share similar intense, and frightening, feelings. In fact, some people within the family, including the heroin user, suffer from an emotional paralysis. By this I mean a feeling of impotence, of being trapped, not knowing which way to move to relieve the tension. The following is a description of some of the discomfort experienced by those having to cope with addiction.

Guilt

Addiction would not be a problem for most addicts if they did not suffer from guilt, because there would be no conflict. It is this feeling, resulting from a niggling awareness of pain caused to others, that often brings reality to the fore and instigates recovery. As well as feeling guilty about the distress of loved ones, many feel guilty because they have become addicted or, under the influence of heroin, have behaved in ways which are not normal for them. As a result of the dependence on drugs, they may have become self-obsessed. They may have used others to their own ends and been insensitive to their feelings. A combination of the denial that behaviour like this happens and a numbing of the senses with heroin, is often used to keep these feelings of guilt at bay.

Very often, recovering addicts need considerable help in coming to terms with their guilt. If they do not, then they may well continue to deal with it by using drugs to anaesthetize the pain. Most guilt comes about through people not accepting the disease concept. If addicts do not see themselves as sick people who need to get well, then they have to see themselves as morally weak or evil. This attitude does not give any hope of recovery. (Please note, I am not using the disease concept to absolve addicts from any responsibility. As you will see in the following chapters, I believe strongly that they should have to accept the consequences of their behaviour whether they are under the influence of drugs or not. If they do not, it lessens the likelihood of their getting well.)

Guilt is a primary feeling from which family members also suffer. Many relatives go through the agonizing process of self-blame and ask themselves, 'Where have I gone wrong? Where have I failed as a parent, partner or child?' I have had eight and nine year-olds ask me if it was because they had been naughty that their mummy started using again. One very adult eleven year-old openly disbelieved me when I tried to reassure him that there was no way he could stop his mother from using drugs. He was riddled with guilt. Different parents have queried if the use of drugs was because they sent their child away to school, or had not sent him away to school; shown too much love, or not enough love; been too strict, or not strict enough. Wives, husbands, lovers have asked if they have been caring enough, understanding enough, too demanding, or good enough in bed. Again, most of the guilt is caused because people do not understand or accept the disease concept. There is no other illness which produces so much self-blame in the family as the addictive disease.

Low Self-Esteem

By the time the addicts ask for help in abstaining from heroin use, they do not like themselves very much. Most chemically dependent people see themselves as failures in their work situation. It is likely that the majority of addicts have not held down any job of work for a long period of time. The addiction keeps interfering with work performance. If they have worked for a considerable length of time, then it is probable that they have at least one other person propping them up or covering up for them. The persistently gnawing awareness of this reality does not improve the self-esteem of an addict.

Close relationships are also another area which causes addicted people to feel inadequate. In the early days the use of heroin or other drugs may have helped them to feel less inhibited or shy, but as the illness progresses it is impossible to maintain close equal relationships which contain mutual honesty, trust and respect. Sexual problems may also occur. Initially use of heroin improves sexual performance, but, like the alcoholic many male addicts find themselves unable to achieve or maintain an erection as the addiction progresses. Many of the women find themselves disinterested in sex, other than as a way of making money or bartering for more drugs.

Relatives and friends also have a very low opinion of themselves, partly as a result of the self-blame or feelings of guilt. The obsession for the addicted person can become so great that family members find it difficult to give much of themselves to their other relationships. It is not unusual for marriages to suffer because at least one parent is too preoccupied with the chemically-dependent child. Other children in the family can feel left out because the addict demands so much attention from their parents. Lovers can feel very inadequate because they have had to take second place to heroin. They may feel that it is their fault that love-making happens rarely and that they have become unattractive. Some partners may find themselves so tense and angry with the addict and the surrounding situation that making love is the last thing they would want to do.

A fixation with addiction can also cause lack of concentration in the work situation. Children find themselves not concentrating at school. They are upset as mummy keeps crying because daddy has disappeared yet again. Wives and husbands find that their work is suffering because their minds keep wandering to the fact that their addict has been arrested for possesion of heroin, or they worry about how they will pay the household bills. Parents are preoccupied with how they can stop the addiction or wondering where that valuable necklace has disappeared and whether they should call the police or not.

Anger

A large number of addicts with whom I have worked have been angry. Many are not aware of the extent of their anger because that feeling has been numbed by heroin. The anger can be at themselves for being addicted, other people for not understanding, fate, providence, or whatever god they believe in, for putting them in this situation. The question is always 'Why has this happened to me? What have I done to deserve this?'

That question is also asked by many relatives. Most relatives of addicts that I see are angry – but denying it. Many are repressing their anger because they feel guilty at having aggressive feelings towards a sick person. Others disown their feelings because they are so intensely painful and frightening; the only way they know how to deal with them is to push them down and try to forget them. The majority of relatives need permission to express their anger constructively. Some may need therapy to help them come to terms with this feeling.

When you think about it, why shouldn't they be angry? Why should anyone be expected to cope with the constant tension, the continual put-downs, the insensitivity to others' feelings, the never knowing what to expect, the total self-centredness, embarrassment, lies, deceit, the playing one family member off against another, and all the worry and loneliness which comes from caring about an addict? How on earth can a person live in a situation like this and not be angry? To their distress, some relatives may have found that, as a result of the tension and the need to control the addict, they have become violent. This results in an increasing of the feelings of guilt, self-hate and fear.

Fear

Most addicts are extremely fearful of what is happening to them through the addiction. Some of the fear is of overdosing or going into withdrawal. Many are frightened of their dependence on the drug, but also frightened of coping with life without it. Most are worried about how they are going to get the money to pay for their next fix. Others are extremely tense because they are living on a knife-edge of deception. As the illness progresses, it becomes more and more difficult to remember all the alibis and keep ahead with the deceitful games. However, fear does not often persuade addicts to cease using heroin. Frequently, it provides another reason for escaping from reality.

There is a parallel with families: they have similar fears of the addict using again, of never knowing what to expect, of not being able to cope with the constant tension, of upsetting him and perhaps making him use again. They also have terror of the addict killing himself, of him being caught by the police or having to go to gaol, of the effect of the addiction on the other children in the family, of what other people think, while they believe albeit wrongly, that it must somehow be their fault.

AN ADDICT'S RELATIVES

In my experience, many of those close to an addict are suffering more than he is. Although he is in a great deal of emotional turmoil, his awareness is impaired by the amount of heroin and other drugs that he has in his system. Family members who are not dependent on drugs or alcohol are having to survive the pain of reality.

I hope I have made it clear that if an addict is to have the opportunity to get well, he is not the only person who will need to change. Relatives have often become involved in the treatment programmes I have worked in with the sole motive of stopping their addict from using. Most are shocked, angry or surprised when I, or one of my colleagues, suggest that perhaps they need some help too. In order to reach drug abusers and help them face the reality of their problem, it often means struggling through the protective shell surrounding that person; that is the cocoon of the family. To achieve this, we have to help those closest to an addict recognize that he is not the *only* problem in the family. The family support system surrounding that person may require some changing; relatives may need to alter their attitudes and behaviour towards the addict, if they want to help. Even if only one person in the family network is willing to see that there are choices, and gradually changes the way he behaves towards the addict, this can have some very positive results.

If that person is you, you do not have to continue suffering constant emotional pain. You can learn to kick *your* habit. You can help by giving up *your* addiction to the addict and, while still caring, leave him free to face reality and make some choices of his own. It is not easy and you will probably need on-going help. *Families Anonymous*, a sister organisation of *Narcotics Anonymous* and a self-help group for relatives and friends of addicts will supply a good deal of constructive advice and support. There you will meet people who are going through, or have been through, situations similar to your own. You will understand and identify with the fear, the feelings of helplessness and despair, the worry and guilt, and the problems in learning to 'let go' of the addict. Also, you should find a message of hope there. Above all, I believe that through involvement with this organization you will find some relief from coming to see that *the heroin dependence is not your fault*.

Whether your addict gets well or not, you, as a concerned person, need and deserve help to recover from this extremely painful family addiction. If you change, it is much more likely that he will want to change too.

4. Valerie – Mother of an Addict

Valerie was a very attractive, well-groomed lady of about fifty years. She had been married for twenty-eight years to Philip, who was a business executive in an international company. Devotedly, she supported him in his work and they had often travelled abroad together on business trips. They obviously cared a great deal for each other and Philip often said that Valerie was the mainstay of his life.

They had three sons, Michael (27) who was a doctor, married with one little girl; Simon (24) a talented musician and Mark (21) who had been at University studying architecture. These five formed a very close, supportive family; together they had survived some terrible tragedies. Ten years ago when they were on holiday, their lovely home was burned to the ground. Three years ago, Simon was very seriously injured in a motorbike accident; he was in a coma for some weeks. Friends of the family say that on both occasions, it was mainly Valerie's strength of character and devotion to her family that pulled them through.

Valerie was a warm, caring person who gave a lot to others. The four men in her family adored her and she had many friends who came to her to share their problems and ask for advice. Although she treated her sons equally, her favourite had always been Mark, the youngest; she had always felt closest to him and believed that they had an open, honest relationship. However, since he went to university two years ago, she was concerned because he had been keeping her at a distance. At first she thought it was just a natural part of growing up, but her concern grew because he looked more and more unwell each time she saw him. When he was questioned about this, he shrugged and dismissed her worry, saying that he had been working very hard at his studies.

After giving some motherly advice about not burning the candle at both ends, Valerie let go of her concerns until some months later when she visited Elizabeth, a long-standing friend of hers. Elizabeth's daughter, Fiona, had been a girlfriend of Mark. They seemed to have drifted apart, though they were at the same university. Elizabeth mentioned that Fiona had been upset because Mark had borrowed £300 from the younger woman last term and had failed to pay it back. Valerie, very embarrassed by this statement, immediately wrote a cheque to cover the debt. She was even more upset when her friend said that Fiona was worried because Mark was associating with a group of students who were notorious for their drug using and other escapades.

At home that evening, she voiced her concerns to Philip who thought she was worrying unnecessarily. However, he did agree that they should visit their youngest son the following weekend to find out what was going on. Mark soon eased their concern. Yes, he had borrowed £300 from Fiona and he had been very irresponsible in not repaying it. His old car had needed some urgent repairs done to it and at the time it seemed easier to borrow the money from his friend than bother his parents. Perhaps Fiona's criticisms about his new friends were because he was spending less time with her and more with a new girlfriend? Yes, he had occasionally used drugs but only marijuana. Everybody in the university did it as did his two older brothers from time to time, and it was as harmless as his mother's daily gin and tonic! Didn't his parents trust him enough to know that he would never touch hard drugs? Valerie and Philip left their son feeling more reassured but somewhat guilty about the doubts they had been having about him.

At the end of term, Mark arrived home to say that he was leaving university. He felt he needed to find a job and discover what 'life' was about. Being a student restricted his growth as a human being, he said. Would his parents be willing to give him some money to tide him over until he found some work? Valerie and Philip were shocked; Philip was extremely angry and at first refused to help Mark, saying that he had thrown away the opportunity of a life-time. It was Valerie who calmed him down and eventually persuaded him to be more supportive towards their youngest son. They helped him find a flat in London and gave him a generous allowance until he was able to find a job. Mark tried several jobs over a few months but did not appear able to settle at any of them. He did not have much contact with his parents during this time.

His brothers, Michael and Simon, visited their parents' home one weekend and confirmed their worst fears – Mark was using heroin. Valerie immediately went up to London and found her youngest son in a dreadful state. He looked ill and unkempt and the flat was in a squalid mess. She brought him home and nursed him through a very uncomfortable withdrawal. They had long talks, became close once again and decided that together they would beat his addiction. For the first time for years Valerie refused to travel abroad on a business trip with her husband. She also protected Philip from a lot of the facts about their son's heroin abuse. She felt he had enough to cope with with his business worries. Valerie paid off all Mark's debts without metioning it to anyone in the family. Unknown to his mother, Mark also borrowed money from his brothers.

The young man started to look much better physically. He found himself a job locally and renewed his relationship with Fiona. Everything seemed to be going very well; then, without a word to anyone, he disappeared. When he didn't come home from work one evening, Valerie phoned one of his colleagues only to discover that he had not been at work at all that day. She went up to his room; all his possessions appeared to be there but she found a syringe in a coat pocket. She discovered later that her account had been overdrawn by several hundred pounds; Mark had forged her signature. Valerie was so shocked and upset that she became ill. Her husband was shattered; Valerie had always been the 'coper' in the family but now she spent most days in tears. She lost interest in the home and she no longer took as much care with her appearance. She spent hours in bed. Her main subject of conversation was Mark. She blamed herself for spending so much time abroad with her husband; she blamed Philip for being too obsessed with his work; she blamed her two older sons for not spending enough time with their younger brother; she lost her friendship with Elizabeth because she blamed the distraught Fiona for having had an argument with Mark before he disappeared. Secretly, she believed the drug-using was her fault. Somehow she had failed as a mother and she must make it up to her son.

Three months later, after no word, a friend of Mark's contacted Valerie and Philip to tell them that their son had been admitted to hospital having over-dosed on heroin. Valerie rushed up to the hospital and against the advice of her other sons, she brought Mark home again. Apart from the fact that Simon and Michael refused to go to their parents' home while Mark was there, the pattern repeated itself, except this time, Mark did not run away from home when he resumed the use of drugs. He found a source of supply locally. He was also using alcohol very heavily when he couldn't afford heroin. His mother, who wanted to believe that as long as he was at home and under her care he would be all right, turned a blind eye to the fact that he was out until all hours, continually late for work and always borrowing money. She was angry at Philip because he just would not try to understand why she was no longer taking such an interest in his business and in him. She accused him of being selfish, self-centred and uncaring about their son. Philip had tried to help; he had talked to their family doctor, a friend of his, and was told that heroin addicts didn't recover. He didn't really believe that Mark was addicted – yet. He saw his youngest son as irresponsible and weak-willed. His eldest son, Michael who was also a doctor, had told them about an organization called *Families Anonymous*, which might be able to help Valerie and him. He didn't see that they needed help. All young Mark had to do was pull himself together and everything would be all right again. Perhaps Mark needed the discipline of the army? It had helped him grow up quickly when he was a lad. However, both Valerie and Mark scoffed at the idea. Valerie saw Mark as being too sensitive a person to cope with the rigours and discipline of being a soldier. Mark was only too happy to agree with her.

The next crisis occurred whe Mark was caught stealing money from his employers. He was fired immediately, although the company did not press charges because the director was a friend of his father's and he wanted to save the family any embarrassment. Again Valerie and Philip had a stormy argument because Philip wanted to throw Mark out of their home. Valerie was terrified that they would lose contact with their youngest son and that he would die from his addiction. She was convinced that as long as he was at home where she could keep an eye on him, he would keep his drug-using to a minimum.

It was Philip who left home after a series of bitter arguments. Michael, in an attempt to bring the family together again and to help his younger brother, recommended a treatment centre which was well known for helping addicts recover. When it was first suggested to Mark, he agreed that it might be a good idea to go there sometime in the future, but his habit was not that bad – yet. In fact, he thought he had conquered it because he had not had a fix for two months. (At that time no-one in the family saw it as significant that he had been drinking extremely heavily during those two months. A few weeks before he had become embarrassingly drunk at a friend's wedding, upsetting several people with loud and lewd comments about the bridesmaids.) But he did agree to go into treatment if he ever resumed the use of heroin. In the meantime, he persuaded his mother that what he needed was a holiday. After all, he had recently been under a lot of stress! Valerie was relieved that he was planning to go with a group of 'sensible' young people and she agreed to foot the bill. She believed that he had earned it by being strong-willed enough to not use those damned drugs.

Actually, although Valerie had an anxious two weeks while he was away, Mark returned from the south of France looking extremely well. He had not used drugs at all during that time, although he had gone to a couple of parties where he got extremely drunk. He omitted to tell his mother that he couldn't remember much of what had happened at one of them. Philip (who was back at home by this time) and Valerie were delighted. Mark had obviously got over the very nasty phase he had been going through. He was even talking about going back to university.

Shortly after Mark returned from holiday, he went up to London for the day and did not return home. Instead he went to visit some of his old friends who were still using smack and within a short period he had developed the habit again. He sold his mother's car which he had borrowed, and moved in with a girlfriend who was also addicted to heroin. Between them, they got throught the £2,500 he got for the car within a month.

Philip and Valerie were beside themselves with anxiety and fear. They had had no word from Mark, they were terrified that he had had an accident, but they did not want to call the police in case it brought attention to his drug-using. They contacted various friends in London and indirectly enquired about Mark, but no-one had seen or heard of him. Eventually, when he ran out of money, Mark telephoned his brother Michael, and pleaded to be taken for treatment. The eldest son went ahead and arranged it, and contacted his parents once it had all been organized. He was anxious that his mother should not assume responsibility for 'fixing' her youngest son again. Once more, he strongly recommended that his parents attend *Families Anonymous* to get some help for themselves. He had been to several meetings and had found it a great help both in dealing with his brother and some of his patients. Valerie and Philip went along to the nearest meeting just to please Michael and also because the treatment centre recommended it. Philip was surprised how much help he got from that meeting – it made a lot of sense to him. Valerie, on the other hand, was furious. Whatever was Michael thinking of? These dreadful people were talking about *letting go* of their addicts! How could she be expected to let go of Mark? According to the literature he had a killer disease. She was not going to stand by and let her youngest son die; she was going to do everything she could to help him stop using heroin! It was her duty and responsibility as a caring mother. She would not be attending any more of those meetings.

Mark did not complete treatment. Two weeks after his admission he discharged himself. The reason he gave his parents was that he felt he had learned enough in the fortnight that he had been in the centre. Everyone else there had much more serious problems than he had, he said, and he recognized that he would end up like them unless he took some serious action. He convinced his mother that he had learned the importance of attending *Narcotics Anonymous.* The other three men in the family were not so willing to believe him as was Valerie. They said nothing to her, but, privately, they resigned themselves to accepting that any attempt to try and get Mark back into treatment would be dismissed by the young man.

Once more Valerie did everything she could to help her son. She found out where the nearest *Narcotics Anonymous* meetings were and reminded Mark of the necessity to continue attending them when she thought he was becoming lax in his involvement. She also found him a job with another friend of the family.

Everything appeared to be going well for several months. Inevitably, the pattern repeated itself; Mark did not return home from work one day. Once more, when Valerie made some enquiries she discovered that he had failed to turn up at work that day. Mark was found that evening – by a policeman. He was dead, as were two other people. Witnesses confirmed that he had been driving under the influence of alcohol and drugs, had taken a corner on the wrong side of the road and had hit an on-coming car head on. He died instantly, as did one of his three passengers and the driver of the other car. The other two passengers escaped with minor injuries.

That fatal accident happened two years ago. Valerie and Philip have been living apart for six months. They are taking divorce proceedings and Philip is planning to marry his secretary. Valerie is still punishing herself for her son's death. She still believes that somehow it is her fault. She had seen herself as a lady with a big capacity for loving and believed that her love for her son should have helped him overcome his dependence on drugs. It had become her mission in life to help him and in her eyes she had failed. After the funeral, Valerie withdrew into herself; she isolated herself from her friends, made little effort to communicate with her husband or her other two sons. She refused offers of holidays abroad or moving to another house. She ate little, has lost two stones in weight and has been treated for depression, in vain. Michael has tried to persuade her to return to *Families Anonymous* but she refuses to do this. Her attitude is that she didn't see how they could help her when Mark was alive – how could they possibly do anything for her now he is dead. They couldn't bring him back to life!

There is no guarantee that if she had become involved with the *Families Anonymous* programme when Mark was still living at home, that he would be alive today – he may have still continued to use drugs. However, Valerie might have had peace of mind and a close relationship with her husband and two sons. Her obsession with her son's addiction has cost her all of that.

The death of Mark and the subsequent break-up of the family is no-one's fault. Everyone within that unit tried to help the youngest son because they cared. However, none of their previous experiences in life had prepared them for knowing the appropriate way to cope with addiction. In their ignorance, they were not aware that their kind of protective loving was destructive to the family as well as to the addict; this realization did not occur to them until it was too late.

5. Robert – Boyfriend of an Addict

Robert is 28 years old and has the reputation of being a skilled and efficient garage mechanic. He is a shy, retiring young man with a warm, gentle sense of humour. No-one was more surprised than he when shortly after he met Carol at a party, he discovered that she was as attracted to him as he was to her. Carol is also 28 years old and is a single parent; she has a daughter, Amy, who is 10. Carol is a nurse; she is a very pretty blonde and seems very vivacious and outgoing. She has had a lot of support from her mother who has helped her bring up young Amy.

Within four months of meeting each other, Robert and Carol decided to live together. Amy was delighted by this because in the short time of knowing each other, she and Robert had become good friends. Amy had not liked Guy, her mother's previous boyfriend. Although Robert knew that Carol's past relationship had been an unhappy one and that she had moved out of London to get away from her lover, no-one had told him of the real reason for her leaving town. Guy was a heroin addict. In the beginning of their relationship Carol had tried to help him with his addiction but had ended up using drugs herself. Eventually, Carol had become very concerned about the effects of her drug use on Amy and the fact that she was becoming less and less able to function at work. Her mother persuaded her to leave town and start a new life. Everybody believed that everything would be all right now that she was away from the influence of Guy. No-one talked about the drug use because they thought it was all in the past. In fact, when

Robert and Carol first met, she had not used drugs for six months.

After moving in with Robert, Carol would occasionally work at weekends, leaving Robert and Amy to have more time to get to know each other. Robert, who liked children, was impressed by Amy's maturity and air of responsibility. Sometimes, he was amused by her maternal attitude towards Carol; it often seemed that it was the child who was looking after her mother. Robert and Amy had an easy relationship but he often sensed her withdrawal into a dream world and her reluctance to discuss the past. He was very concerned by her hysterical behaviour when her mother was late returning home from work one evening. However, it was dismissed by Carol as over-reaction by Amy and the young girl was admonished for behaving like a baby. Apart from this incident and one argument over Carol having too much to drink at a party, the three of them were very happy for several months.

Carol and Amy went up to London to spend a week with Carol's mother. Robert was unable to go because he was working. On their return, he noticed a strained atmosphere between the two females but dismissed it as a mild argument. However, the atmosphere did not improve; Amy kept withdrawing to her room and Carol was in a foul temper and looked very unwell. She said that she thought she had flu. Robert returned home from work one evening a week later to find a note saying that Carol had gone to stay with her mother and had taken Amy with her. Anxiously, he rushed up to London to find out what was going on. When he got to Carol's mother's he was greeted by a weeping Amy and her angry grandmother. Carol was not in the house.

It was then that Robert was informed of Carol's addiction; he learned that the real reason that she had left London to live in his town was that she had had a heroin habit for five years. She believed that if she settled down in a good relationship in a 'nice' town she would no longer need to use drugs. She was convinced that Robert was all she needed to help her stay away from heroin. Unfortunately, on her previous visit to London, she had visited some old friends who were addicts, had used drugs with them and had not returned to her mother's home for two or three days. This was a familiar pattern to both Amy and her grandmother. Whenever Carol wanted to score, she tried to arrange that Amy was with the older woman. It had not always worked out that way and the child had had to cope on her own in the past when Carol and Guy were too stoned to care about her needs or feelings. Robert also learned that Carol had lied to him about her salary; she was earning considerably more than she had stated. Apparently, with the help of her mother, she was paying back some considerable debts. Her bank overdraft alone ran into thousands of pounds.

Robert left the house late that night, numbed with shock. The woman that Amy and her grandmother were describing did not match his Carol whom he saw as honest, responsible and loving, as well as being a good mother. The older woman was suggesting that she was devious, dishonest and extremely irresponsible – and an addict! Yet, he knew that there had been a lot of unanswered questions and what they were saying must be true.

Two weeks later, Robert had had the opportunity to think more clearly. He still had not heard from Carol and according to her mother she did not want to hear from him; she was too ashamed. Robert knew that he loved both Carol and Amy and that he wanted to help. However, he also acknowledged he knew nothing about addiction and that if he was to help his girlfriend, he needed some help too. He knew that an old schoolfriend of his had been in trouble with drugs but appeared to have kicked the habit some time ago. Robert renewed his friendship with this man and received a great deal of help. He was introduced to his wife and was taken to his first *Families Anonymous* meeting. It was there that he learned that Carol had an illness which caused her personality change and that he could do nothing to stop her from using drugs. He also learned that if he wanted to help her, then he had to learn to let go and not enable her to go further into her illness by being overprotective. Robert knew himself well enough to know that he had a very strong tendency towards protecting those he cared for. He shared his concerns after the meeting with his friends who reassured him that if he kept attending *Families Anonymous* and reading its literature, he would receive a great deal of help and support in learning to let go.

Robert went up to London that weekend to visit Amy and her

grandmother armed with a pile of *Families Anonymous* literature. At first the old lady scoffed at the idea of a self-help group but reluctantly promised to read some of the pamphlets. Robert took Amy out for the afternoon and although he intended it to be a time for fun, he found that for the first time during their friendship Amy wanted to talk about the past. He was appalled to learn that she had thought it was her fault that her mother used drugs. She thought she had made her mother very unhappy because she did not like Guy. She had tried very hard but she found him creepy. Often, when Mummy had been working he had other ladies in his bedroom. Also, she had seen him help Mummy put a needle in her arm. Wisely, although Robert found himself getting very angry, he just listened. When she stopped talking, he told her of the meeting he had been to earlier that week where people had explained to him that her Mummy had an illness and that it was nobody's fault that someone used drugs. She used heroin because she liked the feeling it gave her. Amy looked puzzled but seemed reassured when Robert said she could phone him any time when she was worried about her mother.

No-one knew where Carol was for some time. She had phoned her mother a couple of times to check that Amy was all right and then had no further contact for several weeks. Robert continued to attend his meetings and to go up to London most weekends to visit Amy and her grandmother. He was delighted when the older woman announced that she had attended a *Families Anonymous* meeting and had been suprised to find so many mothers who had felt just as she did. She wasn't sure whether she would go back but she would think about it. In fact, Robert started going up to London on Fridays so that she could attend her meetings while he would baby-sit with Amy. The three of them started to have very enjoyable weekends together.

It was during one of those weekends when they were having Sunday lunch, that Carol walked in. She had run out of money and had been sleeping around with various addicts in order to get drugs. She looked unkempt, unhappy and unwell. She was very surprised at the warm reception she got from all three, particularly Robert; she did not expect him still to be involved in her life. After an uncomfortable week during which she withdrew from the effects of heroin, Robert returned and said that he wanted to talk to her.

She listened in amazement as he told her he still loved her, that he had been attending some meetings to get help for himself, that she had an illness and that she could get help with this disease. She reminded him that she was a nurse and because of that she knew she was going to die. Heroin addicts never got better; she was aware of that. Robert told her of his school friend and how he had got well through a group called *Narcotics Anonymous*. Carol was very sceptical about self-help groups; but Amy seemed to have taken it for granted that she was going to attend the meetings and she had let her daughter down more than enough. Her mother had also given her an ultimatum earlier in the week. She had been told that she was welcome to stay at home as long as she stayed off drugs and was receiving help in overcoming her addiction. Mother would not be paying off any of her debts however, that was Carol's responsibility. Robert and the older woman had come to an agreement about sharing the costs of Amy's material needs until Carol had a more stable recovery.

It was really to please the others and also because she was willing to try anything to stay off drugs that Carol attended her first *Narcotics Anonymous* meeting. She sat at the back of the room and just listened. Some of the people there looked really happy; she didn't believe that they were really addicted. Perhaps they had just tried heroin once or twice? However, one very attractive girl, who looked full of the joys of life, started sharing. The more she talked, the more intently Carol listened because what she was hearing was almost a duplicate of her own drug history. Yet, this girl had not touched drugs for two years. Maybe there was some hope for her!

Carol stayed in London for another three months, attending N.A. meetings three or four times a week. She found a nine to five job working in a shop because nursing meant working awkward hours at times. She had a lot of amends to make to Amy and she wanted to be with her as much as possible. Robert kept coming up to London at weekends and she never ceased to be amazed at his devotion to her. Yet, she knew him well enough to know that if she went back to using drugs, he would continue to be friends with Amy but there would be no relationship for them. After spending a week's holiday together, it was agreed that as soon as Amy completed her school year, Carol and she would move back to Robert's home. Amy was delighted; even more so when her mother and Robert got married one year later.

So far, Carol has continued to attend her meetings and has stayed drug-free for three years. Robert has returned to *Families Anonymous*. After Carol started attending *N.A.* regularly, he thought he no longer needed help. However, he discovered that even with Carol's recovery he has an overwhelming need to control and be over-protective; when that happens he and Carol, and sometimes he and Amy, fall out. He has discovered he needs help just to come to terms with himself – not only because he has a close relationship with an addict.

6. Learning to Let Go

During my training as a counsellor, my colleagues and I were screened to see if we would be suitable for working with chemically dependent people. It is a part of my personality to rise to a challenge and working with addicts is just that! Nothing satisfies me more than helping other people, but if I am not careful, I can assume a god-like attitude. In fact, I had been warned by one of my bosses that some people in the helping professions (psychiatrists, psychologists, nurses, teachers, social workers, etc.) can be very destructive in their efforts to help addicts. Like the relations of the addict, we can assume responsibility for his behaviour.

Initially, I, like a number of fellow students, was true to type. In my efforts to help, I tried to control several addicts. I spent hours trying to persuade people who had already made up their minds to discharge themselves from treatment, not to do so. I pleaded, cajoled, reasoned, guilt-provoked and even became angry. I fell into the trap of believing it was my fault if they walked out of the centre or used drugs again. I became obsessed with my work to the extent that I neglected my personal life. Eventually, it was put to me rather strongly that I needed to change my attitudes and behaviour if I wanted to continue working in the addiction field.

It was a huge relief to be told, "Liz, while you are responsible for making the greatest effort to help people that you work with, you are *not* responsible for the outcome." My colleagues went on to point out that the only person I had any control over was myself. I could change my thoughts, my feelings, my behaviour, but I did not have the power to alter those of another.

All I, or any other person can do, is to report to an addict the inappropriateness of his behaviour, let him know what I am prepared, or not prepared, to tolerate and suggest some ways he might change. Having done that, I have to let go. It is his choice if he wishes to listen or act on the advice. Whether we like it or not, we are absolutely powerless over his desire to use drugs. If he does choose to abuse heroin, we are just as powerless over whether he gets hurt or not. No matter how caring and shielding we are, in the process of time he will have to suffer, as the illness is progressive and destructive. I was also advised that if I wished to be an effective counsellor, I had to learn to respect others enough to believe that they could cope with their own pain. Whenever I was being over-protective, I was being disrespectful and assuming I was the only one who could deal appropriately with the pressures. In blocking him from reality, I was depriving him of the right of being placed in a situation where *he* was the one who had to accept the consequences of his behaviour and make his own decisions.

It was hard work learning to let go. Occasionally, I still have to fight my need to have everything neat and tidy and thus have no-one suffering any discomfort; I can still be very impatient in wanting everyone to be happy – immediately! Some days I let go better than others. At least most of the time I can now recognize when I am trying to control people; then I can detach. If I fail to be aware of this omnipotent behaviour, I am surrounded by colleagues who will soon point it out to me! Like many others, when I am working closely with an addict, I need to be open to the suggestions and comments of my co-workers who have a more objective distance. I cannot cope with addiction on my own.

WHAT IS MEANT BY LETTING GO?

Many relatives look at me with blank amazement when I start discussing the need for them to let go. For months or years, they have been struggling painfully with the addiction, trying to find some help for the dependent person. At last, they have found it and they have been advised to detach from the problem which has been the sole focus of their lives for all this time! Yet, if they want to aid the addict, and if they themselves want some peace of mind, they have to be prepared to work through this process. Learning to let go requires gaining knowledge of the principles and concept of 'tough love'. These can be described as follows.

Letting go means learning to think positively.

Many relatives are convinced that there is no way out, that the addict is going to die as a result of the drug abuse. Parents and partners have become trapped in a black pit of despair. Some have even found themselves planning the death of the dependent person because it is believed that that is the only way for everyone involved to find some peace. However, it does not have to be that way, because you do have choices; that means becoming more of an individual in your own right and less of an extension of the addict. You have personal needs which have been neglected because you have been preoccupied with the addiction. You can now start being good to yourself.

If you implement some of the suggestions in this chapter, you will have positive results. Gradually, your self-respect will improve, your hope will grow and your fear will diminish. You will no longer continue to be destroyed by the disease.

Your addict does have a chance of recovery. There are organisations and individuals who do understand addiction and its affects on the family. Some of these are listed at the back of this book.

Letting go is not denying, but accepting the addiction.

In chapter three I described the denial of the family and discussed how relatives can minimise the seriousness of the addiction; how they hide reality from others by feigning a brave front. In addition the main area of delusion for many family members is the belief that they have not been hurt by the addiction.

If you want to ease the situation, you will find it a great relief when you stop pretending all is well. Your addict may not be grateful immediately, but in time it will help both of you if you start facing the problem by doing the following:

1. Stop trying to convince yourself that the drug using is 'not that bad'. Don't be conned into believing that because he doesn't use a needle, he is not addicted. Smoking and sniffing heroin can also be signs of addiction. Find out facts about addiction and decide whether your friend or relative has the illness. If he has, accept that it is a serious problem which may result in death unless he gets help.
2. Start talking calmly and factually to the addict about his drug-use and subsequent behaviour when he is relatively drug-free. The more open you are, the more uncomfortable you will make his use of drugs. Let him know that it is an illness that he is suffering from and that he can recover.
3. Start talking openly to others in the family about your concerns over the addiction. Open up communication again.
4. Start accepting that you are not trapped, you have choices but that you cannot cope with this problem on your own. Contact *Families Anonymous* for help for yourself.
5. Start looking for ways of finding help for your addict outside the family. Mention *Narcotics Anonymous* to him. Contact treatment centres for information. Let him know you are seeking help. Follow through what you say you are going to do.

Letting go is the acceptance of having no control over the addict, or his use of drugs.

Remember that you cannot push the addict into giving up drugs and the outcome of his illness is not in your hands. You can only be responsible for making the effort to help by discussing addiction with him and by giving constructive suggestions. Accepting your powerlessness does not permit giving up or thinking what's the point? It means that:

1. You no longer have to threaten or manipulate or make empty threats like "I will leave you if you use drugs again". In all probability, he will call your bluff. (Only make such comments if you intend to carry them out)
2. You no longer have to nag, preach, coax, bargain or lecture.
3. You no longer have to try to be one step ahead of the addict.

4. You no longer need to search his room or belongings for traces of drugs, or other equipment necessary for the ritual (e.g. singed silver foil, teaspoons, lemons, syringes).
5. You no longer need to check with his friends on how he is behaving.
6. You no longer have to extract promises. Start refusing to accept them. At this point, he cannot keep them. He is not able to regulate his drug-taking and is also unable to control his behaviour when he is under the influence of heroin or other drugs.
7. You no longer have to go searching for him if he disappears.
8. You no longer have to believe that the addiction is your fault or your responsibility.

Letting go is not being protective, but permitting the addict to face reality.

This means that you do not have to stop caring about your dependent person, but that you stop being his caretaker. If you want to help then you have to allow him to accept the consequences of his behaviour. The kindest action in the long run is to let him feel the pain which results from his addiction. If he does not, he is never going to want to change.
Not being protective means:

1. You no longer have to rescue the addict. Remember that every time you save him from legal consequences, call his boss with an excuse for his absence, pay his debts, tell lies to cover for him, make it easy for him to leave treatment against staff advice; or in any other way protect him, you are making his drug-taking comfortable for him. You are preventing him from acknowledging the seriousness of his problem.
2. You no longer have to behave as though you believe he will disintegrate if not treated with great caution and gentleness. Don't pussyfoot around him. Forget about protecting the addict's sensitive feelings. In a non-nagging, factual way, *when he is not stoned* let him know how you, and other people, have been affected by the addiction. Be specific, frank, open and honest. Let him know that you are no

longer taking responsibility for his behaviour. His behaviour is *his* problem, not yours. However, do let him know that you will support any attempt at recovery.

Letting go is not trying to change or blame the addict, but making the most of yourself.

Very often, when there is an addict in the family, he can be used as a scapegoat for other problems. For example, if the children are misbehaving, it is assumed that they are reacting to having an addicted parent; if the family finds itself not coping with paying bills, then he is blamed for squandering all the money; if two people have a difficult relationship, then it is his fault for creating tension; nervous and physical ailments within that group of people can also be made the responsibility of the drug-user. Most or some of these complaints may well be justified, but what is, in fact, happening is that relatives are hiding behind the addiction. They therefore avoid looking at their own behaviour and accepting responsibility for changing themselves. If you want to improve such a situation:

1. Start looking after your own needs. You've been through hell. You deserve some encouraging and loving attention from yourself.
2. Start improving your relationships with the other people you care about. How many relatives have not been receiving the love and care they deserve because they had to be secondary to the addict? How many friends are no longer in touch because of your obsession with him?
3. Start having fun again. You don't have to suffer all the time. That is your choice.
4. Start finding ways in which you can change. Do you like yourself? How have you been reacting to the addict? How have you been coping with your feelings? Would you like to feel better? It is your actions that will make or break you – not what the addict does. *Families Anonymous* will help you to find ways of changing and building up your self-esteem.

Letting go is not trying to fix the addict, but is being supportive and encouraging any of his attempts at recovery.

Part of letting go is learning to balance the way you do *not* condone dishonest, devious or irresponsible behaviour with the way you praise any effort towards recovery. Remember that your addict does not like himself very much. Encouragement is very important and he will probably respond very positively towards it. This does not necessarily mean that he will stop using drugs immediately. It is not within his power to do so. He cannot control heroin. However, some praise may result in him starting to make attempts at giving it up.

To be supportive may involve the following:

1. Letting him know you still care about *him* – it is the addiction you dislike as well as the way he behaves under the influence of mood-altering chemicals.
2. Not paying fines or debts but offering to make a financial contribution towards paying for treatment. If possible offer treatment when he is in pain, not when he is using or is pretending everything is wonderful.
3. Commending responsible behaviour.
4. Encouraging involvement with a support group such as *Narcotics Anonymous*.

Letting go is not cutting yourself off from the addict, but detaching with love.

Many people in a close relationship with an addict assume that there are only two alternatives: to go on tolerating his crazy behaviour, or to divorce him, kick him out of the house or otherwise remove him from their lives.

The assumption here is that family members can only achieve some kind of peace of mind if they totally cut themselves off from the addict. Usually, tranquillity is the last thing they find because the action is provoked by a lingering anger and a sense of defeat. Another belief is that if the addict is rejected by the family, then he will be on his own, thus forcing him to reach a *rock bottom* and ask for help. However, addicts are very skilled at finding people who will feel responsible for them. Often, throwing him out or detaching with anger results in him being protected by another individual or group of sympathetic people who do not understand addiction and who thus perpetuate the illness.

If you wish to initiate recovery, there is another choice. The third way involves coming to terms with the fact that no-one can change another person, that caretaking does not cause healthy change in anyone. It requires putting into practice many of the suggestions described in this chapter. It also demands that you stop viewing and treating your addict as a weak or evil person. He is a *sick* person who needs to start to recognise how ill he is before he can start to get well. The person you once loved is still there, he has just been disguised by the heroin in his system.

As a last resort, it may be that the second alternative has to be followed through, especially if other people, perhaps children, are being damaged. Even then, I would recommend offering a choice between treatment or rejection. Many addicts start to want recovery once their backs are up against a wall. The majority of people who request treatment for addiction do so because they have been placed in a situation where they have no other choice. Despite the fact that this is their only motivation (initially) most of these persons do get well.

Letting go means no longer having to be a puppet.

Where family members believe that they ought to be in control of the drug-taking, in reality they are having their strings pulled by the addict. Do not forget that this man is suffering from a serious illness. Very often, his drug-influenced thinking is not very sane. He needs your behaviour as an excuse to rationalize his dependence on heroin. At times, it seems he actually wants you to be angry and fearful of, or for, him. He may go out of his way to make you lose your temper, then he can use your aggression to justify his continuing use. Also, he may take your love and fear for granted by stealing from you and expecting you not to say anything. If this behaviour continues over a period of time, and you avoid discussing it or don't take any action, that is your responsibility. You have condoned it by ignoring it. You do not have to be a puppet. You no longer have to allow yourself to be treated with disrespect. You can improve your own self-respect and help him in the process by practising the following:

1. Do not let him convince you that his addiction is your fault. Keep in mind that he has an illness. You have no more power over making him an addict then you have in making him suffer from cancer, leukaemia or any of the other serious diseases.
2. Do not let him intimidate you by demands, threats or anger. If you give in, or give way to an emotional scene, you have allowed him to manipulate you. Be calm, concentrate on what is right for you, ask for more time to make your decision, call someone in *Families Anonymous* for help, if you feel the need.
3. If something of value is missing and you know the addict has helped himself to it, make him aware that you know. Ask him to replace it or pay it back. If necessary, and if the stealing continues, call the police. I appreciate that this is an extremely painful stand to take against a loved one, but, if you do not take some action and he believes he has got away with it this time, he will probably do it again. Remember, in all likelihood, he is using the money to buy drugs. If you pretend it hasn't happened, you are overlooking the seriousness of his illness. If the addict sees you are willing to assert yourself, he is less likely to abuse your love in this way again. When you start looking after *your* needs and reacting in a healthier way, he is forced to make some changes of his own.

Letting go is not regretting the past nor worrying about the future, but enjoying today for what it is.

Recently I saw a cartoon of a man being squeezed painfully between his guilt from yesterday and his worry for tomorrow. It reminded me of many of the relatives of addicts whom I meet in the course of my work. So many of them have forgotten what it is to have enjoyment or peace of mind. I often ask them, 'When did you last have some fun?' This is usually greeted with suspicious indignation and disbelief that enjoying oneself is possible in the circumstances. Many are weighed down with guilt and have not yet learned that they need to forgive themselves for not coping with the addiction as well as they thought they should. They continue to berate themselves for not knowing better; yet how could they know what to do? In our society there is little understanding or education about how to react appropriately to an addict. Most people in the family respond to the drug abuse because they care deeply and because they want to help. When they are regretting past behaviour, they are not giving themselves credit for having responded with love.

We cannot know what is going to happen tomorrow or next week or next year. We may not be here then. We have been given today and we can choose to be contented with out lot, or miserable in it. I firmly believe that no other person can make us unhappy. If I am miserable it is my reactions and thoughts which cause those feelings. In order to be at ease with myself and others I have to let go and not believe that I am responsible for other people's happiness or for keeping them alive. Over time, I have learned that when I am angry or unhappy, it is usually because I am vainly trying to control one person, a group of persons or a situation.

Many relatives do not believe that they can enjoy life while the addict is still suffering. That is their choice. They do not have to allow themselves to be pulled down into the pits of despair with him. Who knows? If he sees them having fun, he may want to join them. That could be the incentive that makes him want to get well. He may want what they have found – peace of mind!

PROCESSES OF GRIEF

I become very concerned by the high expectations that some relatives have of themselves when they first start letting go. Very often , they grab hold of the philosophy as if it were a life-line and expect to be able to put it into practice immediately. When they fail, they indulge in self-recriminations and even give up. They forget that they have been practising the role of caretaker for many years. It is just as impossible for relatives to completely change their role overnight, as it is for an addict to give up drugs and find complete serenity in the same space of time. On the whole, human beings do not like change.

Many of us get trapped in what is known as the 'security of known misery'; that is, convincing ourselves that there is no point in altering the situation because we may end up being just as unhappy, anyway. There is a terrible security in being close to an addict. He may disappear for days or weeks at a time, abuse your love, steal from you, blame you for his addiction; yet, at the back of each relative's mind there is the knowledge that he needs you. Making a decision to give up being his caretaker requires instigating changes. Certainly, it means the beginning of a new, healthier relationship with the addict but, at the same time, it is the death of the old one.

To sum up, please do not believe that everything is going to be marvellous as soon as you start to let go of your addict. For a period, it may be difficult. He will not appreciate the change, initially. He may well try every game he knows to cause guilt feelings and make life uncomfortable for you. His use of drugs may increase. Try to look at that positively. He may suffer some discomfort but that could push him into seeking recovery. Please remember also, there is no guarantee that he will recover, but it is much more likely when the surrounding family system becomes healthier in its attitude towards the addict. Whether he recovers or not, the philosophy of letting go will help improve the other relationships in the family and they deserve that opportunity. Not everyone needs to be dragged down by the addiction.

Coming to terms with the end of the old relationship will mean that you have to suffer some grief. You may find yourself denying that you are powerless over the addict; you may fight this to such an extent that you become extremely angry – at yourself, at the addict and at life itself. It is possible also that you will try some bargaining like: 'I accept that the programme you suggest works – for other people. I've seen it happen – but – are you sure there isn't *something* I can do to stop him using?'

Depression can also set in. People need to cry as a way of relieving the intense feelings they have been suffering over the time of their awareness of the addiction. For some, the depressed period can last for a long time and they may need therapy. For many, it is a relatively short stage before they go on to surrender the fight, let go of the addiction and start to form more fulfilling lives of their own. It does get better, in time. I have even heard people in *Families Anonymous* say, with serenity, that while they would never wish drug addiction on anyone, they have found some gratitude for the experience of living with it. Eventually, through the self-help group, they have been given the opportunity to find a contentment in life which had been missing – even before the effects of heroin use. That very positive frame of mind comes from learning to let go!

REVIEW OF THE PRINCIPLES OF TOUGH LOVE

Life will get easier if you gradually change your attitude and responses to your addict. In order to adopt the philosophy of letting go you have to evaluate your priorities and take the following steps:

1. Learn to think positively and have hope that life will improve.
2. Do not deny, but accept the addiction.
3. Accept that you have no control over the addict or his use of drugs.
4. Stop being protective, and permit the addict to face reality.
5. Make the most of yourself rather than trying to change or blame the addict.
6. Be supportive and encouraging of any of the addict's attempts at recovery.
7. Do not cut yourself off from the addict, but detach with love.
8. No longer allow yourself to be a puppet – be your own person.
9. Try to live in today and enjoy it. Let go of the past and the future.

7. Recovery is More than just Kicking the Habit

Making the decision to stop taking heroin is only the beginning of recovery. Many addicts and their relatives assume that the only hurdle to cross is getting the drug out of the system. They are shocked and surprised to learn that recovery means rehabilitation; that is learning a new and responsible way of life.

Most users of heroin started taking drugs in their teens. They found that as well as making them feel good, the chemicals helped ease the pain that reality deals out to most human beings, especially in the process of growing up. Maturity comes through facing those hurt feelings and working through them. Those who have escaped from reality through using drugs have stunted their emotional growth. Your addict may have been in this world for twenty-two or even thirty-five years: if he started being dependent on drugs at fifteen, then, emotionally, he is still about that age. It is possible for him to catch up with his peers. However, that means coping with rapid and uncomfortable growth as well as abstention from heroin.

Recovery from addiction is an exploration; it is a process of discovering one's values, beliefs and feelings. It is the coming to terms with, and the acceptance of who you are, eventually finding some peace of mind. Obviously, this cannot be achieved overnight, nor in a few weeks' involvement at a treatment centre, or in *Narcotics Anonymous*.

Over the past two years, as well as working with families, I have also been involved in giving aftercare support – a necessary part of the treatment programme. My colleague and I recommend that our patients should treat the first twelve months of recovery as a therapeutic year. (By this, I do not mean that they should be pampered and tucked up in bed!) During that period, recovery must take precedence over all other factors in life. Many people jeopardize the possibility of getting well by trying to achieve too much, too soon. Some feel pressurized by well-meaning relatives who anxiously want to prove to the world that their addict is normal. It is necessary for recovering addicts to find a feeling of well-being by seeking gainful employment and by restoring relationships. However, it must be done gradually. Recovery, like the disease, is progressive.

Some people may use this attitude of easy does it and give in to their fears and feelings of inadequacy. They opt out of not taking responsibility for maintaining their rehabilitation. This way of behaving is as dangerous as that of the over-zealous person. The restoration of a healthy attitude requires working steadily at finding a responsible and balanced way of life.

Please note that I do not use the term 'recovered'. As I said in chapter two, there is no known cure for addiction. People who have been dependent on heroin and have achieved a lengthy period of abstinence, can still relapse after many years. Inevitably, if this happens, they resume their dependence on heroin from where they left off and it takes over the control of their lives again. Recovery is a way of life that has to be worked at, constantly. An addict cannot afford to be complacent or believe that he has the addiction beaten. It could so easily result in his death. Hence my use of the adjective 'recovering' rather than 'recovered'. It gives no illusion of false hope, since it illustrates the progressive nature of getting well.

THE RECOVERING ADDICT'S DEVELOPMENT OF AWARENESS

For me to be comfortable with myself, I have to become more aware of what I am. To achieve this awareness, I have to learn to recognise what I am sensing, thinking, feeling, and wanting, as well as how I am behaving and how my behaviour affects other people. These are all an integral part of me and my life, but they are not always within my awareness. People who have been using heroin and other drugs for a period of time are far less aware of what is happening within them than are non-addicted people. Some argue that drugs have given them new awareness, but this is synthetic; it is not the coming to terms with reality that is necessary for finding peace of mind. The recovery process has to include discovering the ability to live with one's self. Otherwise, relapse is imminent.

Becoming aware of the senses

Many of my recovering friends tell me that one of the greatest pleasures in becoming well is to re-discover the value of our five senses of sight, hearing, smell, taste and touch. In the past, heroin has blunted or blocked those awarenesses. I hear endless tales of walks in the country appreciating beautiful views, the sounds of the birds or the sea, the feel of the wind or the sun, and the smell of the grass or the flowers. It is often told with such enthusiasm that it almost seems to be a new experience. During the heroin-obsessed days, those simple pleasures have passed many drug-users by.

Becoming aware of the value system

I have mentioned in previous chapters that an addict's thinking is almost totally preoccupied by his drug of choice; also, that addiction often demands living a life-style which is opposed to his value system. The buying and possessing of heroin is illegal. Therefore, anyone who is addicted to that substance is automatically involved in unlawful behaviour. In order to maintain the dependence, a dishonest and devious way of life has to be adopted. This can include lying to loved ones and stealing from them. A heroin addict's life-style is moulded around short-term pleasure-seeking. Sexually, many are promiscuous since the drug lowers inhibitions. Any guilt or conflicting feelings arising from these actions are quickly submerged by the denial system or by using large quantities of drugs.

As well as coming to terms with guilt, it is important for many addicts that they recognise and accept their feelings of shame. Many people believe that these emotions are one and the same; in fact they are quite different, though often intermingled. Guilt is a feeling of exteme regret for past behaviour. It arises from breaking or twisting some 'rule'. Shame occurs when a self-expectation is not reached. Many addicts feel worthless and lacking because they have fallen short of their personal code of ethics. This results in a sense of inadequacy, leading them to believe that they have fallen from grace.

A necessary part of a recovering addict's learning to be comfortable with himself is the discovery, or re-discovery, of his beliefs and value system; identifying what an American friend calls her eternal and internal 'guiltometer'. Each person has to learn to tune into this individual conscience and live by its demands. Like any other human being, an addict is not going to be at ease, nor is he going to find self-respect until he discovers what is right for him. This is usually found by experience, not by being preached at by others. After a period of adjustment, those who have kicked the habit can turn out to be very moral and honest people.

Becoming aware of feelings

Perhaps one of the most frightening issues of becoming well is the acceptance of 'normal' human feelings like fear, resentment, or love. Many people used drugs to hide away from the discomfort they caused. Recovery does not make those emotions disappear. In fact, after the drugs have been out of the system for a short period of time, they have a nasty habit of flooding back with an overwhelming intensity. In the early days of being drug free, some may experience panic attacks. These can be alarming but can be worked through by phoning or visiting a friend who understands the illness.

It is important that recovering addicts do learn to recognise and deal with negative feelings. Two of the main reasons for the resumption of using drugs are repressed anger and low self-esteem. Shyness may also be a problem for some. It is easy to chat up a member of the opposite sex, or show affecton, under the influence of drugs. Sobriety can bring restrained feelings. The anticipation of making love can be frightening because many young addicts only become sexual beings with the aid of drugs. Many have not been sexually active except when intoxicated.

The support of a self-help group like *Narcotics Anonymous* is extremely important in coping with the day to day problems in recovery. There are a number of people in that organisation who have experienced some years of being totally drug-free. Every newcomer needs their support both individually and in group discussions. Having someone identify with the fears and share how they have overcome them, is an essential part of getting well. It is a big step forward in the process of getting well when an addict asks for help. Another important achievement occurs when he listens to people who understand the disease and acts on their advice. The philosophy of *Narcotics Anonymous* is based on mutual caring and support and this gives the much desired feeling of 'I can help: I am needed, therefore I am worthwhile'.

Becoming aware of the need to make decisions

The ability to make plans and stick to them is rarely a strong characteristic in young addicts. In their using days, the main decisions were centred around the drugs. Any other major plans were usually made the responsibility of relatives or close friends. Rebuilding a constructive life can only happen when you know in which direction you want to aim. Many people know that they want to recover from their addiction, but beyond that, they find it very difficult to devote themselves to any plan because they do not know who they are or what they want. Some addicts will complicate issues by trying to keep as many options open as possible; commitment can be a terrifying thing.

Coping with twenty-four hours can be a complicated exercise in itself because most of these youngsters have not had any structure in their lives for a long time. Some find it helpful to introduce the discipline of writing out a list of daily tasks and ticking them off as they achieve them. Major, long-term decisions like what career to pursue, or whether to get married or divorced, may need to be postponed for some time until the individual is sure of what he wants.

Frustrated relatives may find this one of the times when they forget about the principles of 'letting go'. It is not helpful to organize the recovering addict. If you do, you are depriving him of the opportunity of being responsible for his own life. However, if asked, there is no harm in making constructive suggestions.

Like the rest of us, he needs to make mistakes so that he can learn from them. Decision-making improves with time and practice, by bouncing ideas off relatives, and off recovering friends; it also becomes easier with a growing self-respect.

Becoming more sensitive to others

I had toothache the other day and I am sure that I was a pain in the neck to my friends and colleagues. The discomfort preoccupied me and, as a result, I was unaware of, and insensitive to, what was happening to other people. Addicts have been obsessed with their discomfort for a long time and because of this have rarely been sensitive to the needs and feelings of others. The early stages of recovery can also be a time when people's minds are full of themselves. The novelty of feeling well, the fear of not making it, or the adventure of recovery can claim most of their attention. Some relatives, who have been hoping and praying for a miracle, may find that they are disappointed because the recovering addict is still 'into himself'.

It takes time to learn to be less self-centred. Some people can be on the defensive, covering feelings of guilt, shame and fear. As a result, in early recovery, they appear to others as aggressive or ungrateful; others can be withdrawn or hesitant. Patience is a virtue needed by both addicts and their relatives in these early days.

Learning to fill the void

Drugs are the centre of the universe for every practising heroin addict. The decision to do without them leaves a huge, empty space in his life. Although he comes to recognize that if he wants to live, there is no choice, abstinence means the end of his most important relationship. This heroin dependence may have been extremely destructive yet, for some time it has been his main reason for living. Inevitably, recovery brings a feeling of deprivation and mourning, not only for the loss of mood-altering chemicals, but for the end of the life-style which accompanies drug-addiction. There is no way that an addict can remain totally abstinent and still associate with his using friends or hang around his old haunts. Recovery is possible only if he becomes involved with people who are 'winners'.

As they work through this period, some young people find that they have phases of euphoric recall, remembering only the pleasurable feelings. They may even wrongly convince themselves that they were not *really* addicted after all. In an attempt to fill the void, others will seek the excitement they are missing by getting deeply emotionally involved with another (perhaps before they are ready to cope with it). Some will continue to use sex as they did drugs – seeking instant gratification without looking at the long-term consequences. A few will throw themselves into their chosen career, becoming workaholics and hiding from their fears by keeping busy.

One of the strong tendencies of an addicted person is to be rather extreme in his behaviour; this can carry on into recovery. Relatives say to me, 'So, what is different? I rarely saw him in the past because he was always chasing drugs; I seldom see him now because he is forever attending those *N.A.* meetings. He may well be abstinent but there appears to be little benefit as far as the family is concerned'.

Again, it takes time for a recovering person to find the right balance. Obviously, if he is attending meetings twice a day, seven days a week, other important areas of his life, like family, work and social activities, are being ignored. (But there are times, please note, like very early in recovery and following a relapse when this depth of involvement is necessary.) His obsession with heroin has been replaced by a more positive hunger for recovery. Nevertheless, he has to learn that life is even more fulfilling if he gives some priority to restoring family relationships, finding some gainful employment, having some fun socially, as well as being involved in self-help groups.

Narcotics Anonymous states that their organisation is based on a spiritual programme. Some have been known to reject *N.A.* because they have confused spirituality with religion. In his pamphlet *What is Spirituality?*, Paul Bjorklund states: 'Spirituality has to do with the quality of our relationship to whatever or whomever is most important in our life.' The focus of an addict's life has been heroin and other drugs. Heroin has been his god. The challenge of recovery is to find a new god; something must replace drugs as the centre of that person's life. The twelve steps of the *Narcotics Anonymous* programme provide many individuals with just that. For many addicts seeking recovery, the fellowship, mutual caring and structure of the programme and suggested way of life is enough to fulfil the need for a more positive spiritual centering. Others combine this with a like-minded, additional spiritual programme and find that it enhances their recovery.

In addition to the total abstinence from all mood-altering chemicals; one definition of recovery from addiction is the discovery of a feeling of wholeness. This requires us to look at what we want out of life (emotionally, spiritually, socially, physically and intellectually); then deciding how effective we are being in achieving it and implementing changes within ourselves in order to meet our needs. Obviously, recovery is not instant; it is a life-time's work, but, taking it a day at a time, it is possible to work towards that goal gradually. In this way addicts have the opportunity to experience being a whole person; something that many non-addicted persons never find.

Not everyone has to cope with all the problems mentioned in this chapter. I have deliberately mentioned as many of the possible difficulties as I can. So many people have been taken unawares by the early stages of recovery because they have not been forewarned. The majority of young addicts enjoy recovery despite these hurdles; many come to view them as challenges. Their self-esteem benefits and grows rapidly as they work their way through them. They do not need to be protected, just encouraged in their progress. If relatives and friends are supportive but not over-protective, and the addict continues to recover, then relationships can only improve – with time.

8. Coping with a Recovering Addict

Recovery of the addict obviously brings a great deal of joy to everyone concerned. It is the beginning of a period of hope when life is going to take a turn for the better. There is a tentative belief that the addicted person is going to have the opportunity to find a fruitful way of life. It is also a time when people around the addict can learn to relax and be more loving, because a lot of the tension has gone. In my experience, however, it never happens that all the benefits of recovery are reaped immediately. Yet, many relatives expect this.

It would be very unfair, and very unrealistic, of me to lead you to expect that everything is going to be wonderful immediately the addict kicks his habit. I have seen too many people disillusioned by the early stages of recovery. After the years of obsession, pain and anguish, loved ones are often dismayed that recovery does not immediately reach up to their expectations and that they have to struggle through even more changes. Sadly, some give up. I can promise you that life does improve, relationships do become closer, but as well as the addict staying abstinent, it often requires some profound readjustments in the family.

MARY AND CLAUDIA

Mary lives in the United States; her daughter, Claudia aged 29, has been based in London for six years. Claudia has been recovering from heroin dependence for one year. She started using drugs when she was sixteen. Despite the geographical distance and the obvious prolonged trauma, the two women have stayed remarkably close throughout the addiction. On many occasions during the drug-using days, Claudia would make expensive, reverse-charge trans-Atlantic calls for help. Her mother would patiently counsel her over the telephone, she financially bailed her out of trouble more than once.

Mary is a director of quite a large business. She has a powerful personality and believes she can cope with her own problems without any help. She did attend a *Families Anonymous* group once, but she could not see how it would help her. Now that Claudia had freed herself from her dependence on drugs, she did not see that she had a problem at all.

After the younger woman had been recovering from addiction for about nine months, she went home to New Jersey for weeks and was amazed to discover that her mother had bought her an apartment, a car and had arranged a job for her with friends. Several 'suitable young men' were invited round for drinks and dinner parties.

It was obvious that Mary planned that her daughter should stay on in the United States. In the old days, Claudia had been quite happy to let her mother organize her. However, even in her relatively brief period of recovery, she had discovered that she enjoyed being responsible for her own life. The younger woman had never disagreed with her mother except when under the influence of drugs. It took a lot of courage for her to decline her mother's help.

Mary was shocked; it had not occurred to her for one moment that Claudia would not want to stay near her. She reluctantly accepted that after the end of the vacation her daughter would return to England. Sadly, even that came sooner than originally anticipated because Claudia found her mother's controlling behaviour overpowering. Inexorably, the two women fell out because Mary objected to Claudia spending time with an ex-boyfriend of whom she did not approve.

After three weeks, Claudia returned to London leaving her mother extremely upset. She had been pleased to see the younger woman looking well and appearing more sure of herself, but she had not been ready for the dramatic change in her daughter.

There were a variety of reasons for Mary's inappropriate

behaviour. Firstly, although she had been greatly involved in the trauma of the addiction, she had not been prepared for, or included much in, the recovery process. Her expectations were that all problems would disappear as soon as Claudia stopped using drugs. Mary had always treated her daughter as though she was irresponsible and unable to make decisions. When Claudia was taking heroin, she encouraged her mother's over-protectiveness, so much so that the older woman believed that this was the established pattern of their relationship.

The second reason for her insensitive behaviour came from fear. Although she had hoped and prayed for years that Claudia would cease using drugs, she never really believed it would happen. Unconsciously, she had been preparing herself for her daughter's death. Recovery appeared to have established itself but Mary was too frightened to believe it; she was fearful in case it was a phase that would not last. She wanted to prevent her daughter from further agony. As a result, her overbearing love almost cost her their relationship.

Fortunately, Mary is pragmatic by nature and the pain that the rift caused made her decide that she needed to look at her own behaviour and find some help. Recently, she has been more involved with *Families Anonymous;* Claudia and she are communicating again. Slowly, they are learning to get to know each other. This relationship looks as though it may grow and develop in a positive way. Sadly, in some families, recovery of the addict can bring painful conflict even where a close relationship has been maintained during the chaotic heroin-using days. Recovery demands altering relationships within the family. Sometimes relatives, although they dearly want the addict to be well, do not wish to look at the fact that they too may need to change.

I have already written several times that addiction is no one's fault and that it is the addict's choice if he uses drugs again. However, I do believe that many well-meaning and caring relatives can undermine an addict's recovery through their own fear of change. It is one of the saddest experiences in my work to watch a patient make the painful decision to move away from a loving family or close friends because they are helping to make his recovery extremely difficult. Nevertheless, if it is obvious that loved ones are not willing to change their attitudes, and if the addict has tried his hardest to cope with the problem, I will support his decision to leave, just as I always support any heartfelt decisions. These relationships may be renewed or restored at a later date when the addict feels stronger in his recovery. It is also true that relatives may well benefit from having a breathing space in which to do some introspective thinking.

In the early stages of recovery many people involved with an addict will, in common with the addict, find themselves going through an interval of euphoria; this is often called the 'honeymoon period'. It is a well-deserved time of joy, and gratitude that the addict is recovering. To maintain that feeling of well-being, however, means that the family will need to be prepared for a great number of changes in the way that each person reacts to the addict. (Incidentally, this period is made much easier if those involved can see themselves as people in the process of recovery from the family illness and needing the help and support of a self-help group like *Families Anonymous*.)

CHANGE OF RULES

Every family needs to have a set of rules so that each individual can function as a member of that group. They may not be written down or even verbalized, but each person knows what to expect from the system. Questions like: Who is the chief decision-maker? Who answers the telephone? Who provides the family income? What time is dinner? need answers. In some families, these rules are negotiated from time to time and changed; in others, the same old rules go on applying for years.

In a family which includes a using drug addict, there is an additional set of unwritten or unspoken regulations which have developed throughout the process of the disease. Such rules may include:

1. The addict has the primary consideration in this family. Everything is organised to function around him.
2. We do not say anything to the addict which may upset him.
3. Mother is the main person to take responsibility for the addict. She looks after him, makes most of his decisions and

will delegate responsibility to others when she has other unavoidable commitments. He is unable to be responsible for himself.

4. We do not talk outside this family about the addiction. To do so would be extremely disloyal.
5. Any socializing must exclude the addict in case he causes embarrassment.
6. We do not want to cause any more upset in this family so we do not tell each other our personal fears and worries.
7. We must do everything we can to make the addict stop using drugs.

These silently acknowledged, but established guidelines provide some kind of security. Everyone knows what behaviour to expect from everyone else – including the addict. True, he may be difficult to live with at times, he may even disappear for weeks or months but the family and other concerned persons generally know that he will return. Remember, he needs the help of his family; he cannot function as a practising addict without his support system. Within that family, the relationship patterns become very rigid and fixed. Everyone knows what role to play – disciplinarian, passively quiet adjuster, tension reliever, saviour or peacemaker. Each time he gets into trouble with drugs, the same scene is enacted over and over again with everyone playing their part. Very little changes, except perhaps the feelings become more intense over time.

If you take the addict out of that system, what happens? Confusion—because the rules do not apply any more. Recovery of the addict means that the family has lost one of its key members. He looks the same, but he is behaving differently; he is being responsible so he no longer needs looking after; he is coping with his life so there is no more need to be obsessed about him. Quite suddenly, regulations and relationships need to change. Everyone is floundering because the old, terrible security has disappeared. How are people to react? What do we talk about now that addiction is no longer the topic of the day, or the month, or the year? Why (when this is all I've prayed for) am I so fearful, and feeling lost and inadequate?

CONFLICTING FEELINGS

Many people involved with an addict find that, though they have gained what they really wanted (the recovery of the addict), they are also experiencing feelings of loss. Sometimes these emotions are hidden deep inside and take years to surface. When any major change happens in life, it is inevitable that we have conflicting feelings. Take for example, a woman who has been single for some years and who eventually forms a partnership with the man she loves. While she experiences joy and contentment in that relationship, she also finds herself missing some of her individual freedoms. Similarly with a man who has been unhappy in his marriage for a long time: he leaves home and though he knows he made the right decision, finds himself mourning the loss of his wife.

It is possible for relatives of an addict to experience great relief over his recovery and yet miss the old, familiar life-style. Although it was painful, there were attractions to living with his addiction. For some, the main positive feelings come from being needed by the addict. Recovering addicts are more independent and more responsible; this can leave family members feeling no longer needed and of little worth. Unless they find other areas of their life where they can build up their self-esteem, recovery of the addict can bring feelings of fear and depression.

Several friends and relations receive a great deal of praise from others while living with addiction. ('I don't know why you put up with it. I think you're marvellous.') When the addict becomes well, the approving comments are transferred to him. Relatives can find themselves feeling left out and resentful that he is yet agan the centre of attention, in recovery. ('Why can't people see that I suffered as much pain as he did?')

The conflict of experiencing gratitude and intense anger can also be confusing and frightening. Some may come to mistrust their own feelings. It is very common in early recovery for relatives to undergo extreme bitterness and resentment, especially if they have coped with the addiction by submerging all their feelings. Quite often, these surface when the recovering person is only just beginning to live responsibly, taking it one day at a time. Frustrated and insecure relatives may insist that he atone for all the damage done in the past—immediately.

The level of trust, which is already understandably low, diminishes even further because the addict can only cope with making amends gradually. Sometimes, because they are feeling bad, relatives can resent the addict for starting to feel good. When in pain, it is a very human response to try and make others feel as much discomfort as we do. Dismayed at their own inadequate responses, some relatives will go on to predict the failure of the recovery process, or point out where they think the addict needs to make improvements, rather than looking at themselves and making some changes in their attitudes and behaviour. Usually, all this painful struggle results from a feeling of uncertainty, of not knowing what to expect from others or from recovery and of no longer knowing how to react.

POWER STRUGGLE

Trust is a sensitive area within many of the families of recovering addicts. Many feel guilty that they are still suspicious of their addict's behaviour and worry that the lack of trust will undermine his confidence and, as a result, his recovery. Most recovering addicts are aware that they have to earn the confidence of other loved ones and that this will take a long period of time. So often in the past promises have been broken by the addict and he has resumed his use of drugs. It is only to be expected that relatives will be wary and watchful in the early stages of recovery. If the family is to learn to function in a healthy way, it will need a lot of support in practising the principles of letting go at this stage. Lack of trust can easily lead to a return the old behaviour of trying to control the addict.

Many recovering people alter as Claudia did. As a practising addict, she was very skilled at playing the 'fragile little girl' and manipulating others into feeling responsible for her. With recovery, she made changes and tried to establish an equal, sharing relationship with her mother. Many relatives find themselves fearfully unable to do this because surrendering the power means allowing themselves to be vulnerable again. ('If I trust him and give him the responsibility within the family that he is requesting, he may let us down and then we will all be in a mess again. Perhaps it is better that I stay in charge for a little while longer.')

Another way that family members can keep themselves in a very powerful position is to act as the addict's therapist, by keeping a check on his behaviour and counselling him on how he should think, feel and act. Serious and painful conflict can arise amongst many couples (whether these be parent/child or man/woman relationships) when each is trying to gain power over the other by being obsessed about how the other should change. Easy relationships only develop when each has learned to let go of the other and allows him to be responsible for himself. He should also be prepared to assess his own progress and make some gradual changes of attitude and behaviour.

Some families can go to the opposite extreme and give the addict too much power within the family circle. Usually, this is a result of continuing fear and the prolonged belief that anything they might say could cause conflict and make the addict use again. As a result, there is no dialogue, no negotiating of roles and they pander to his expectations in case they rock the boat. There is no chance of mutual trust developing in this kind of relationship because it continues to be dominated by fear.

A great many relationships do survive and blossom as a result of the struggles of early recovery. Those that have achieved most success have resulted from not having too high expectations too soon, from recognizing recovery as providing a new relationship which needs time to develop, from the gaining of mutual respect and honesty, from the slow development of trust, from the growth of open communication, and from the recognition and acceptance that each person involved needs to make some adjustments.

9. Relapse

Addiction is a chronic, terminal illness which can be arrested. However, like a number of progressive disorders, the danger of relapse is ever present. The potential for the return to active addiction is always there, apparently for life. Therefore it is absolutely necessary to encourage total abstinence as the only goal for a recovering addict and yet, be prepared to use *tough love* to help those who do resume the use of mood-altering chemicals. A number of those relapsing will learn from the experience, redouble their efforts on their recovery programme, get well and remain that way. Others may suffer a series of relapses, gradually improving over time and eventually finding a peaceful recovery. Unfortunately, there are still others who may never recover and who will eventually die from this illness.

WHAT CAUSES RELAPSE?

Many relatives live in fear of their addict using drugs again and will go to any lengths to stop them from being tempted. They may choose not to have alcohol in the home, or they may become very active in trying to get rid of the addict's pushers by finding out all the details and reporting them to the police, or they may spend hours of their time watching the addict and checking up on him in case he strays from the narrow path. It may be appropriate to take some of these actions anyway, but often the decisions are made because the fearful assumption is that the addict will have a sudden urge to use drugs again; the belief being that the best way to help him is to remove any dangers.

I have heard many addicts and their relatives use the term 'slip' when referring to a relapse. It is a word that I tend to avoid using because it indicates a sense of suddenness and even implies that the taking of drugs was an accident. Relapse rarely happens on the spur of the moment and it is hardly ever accidental. It is true that many addicts will find themselves having the urge to use drugs again in early recovery as it takes time for the body to adjust to continued abstinence from heroin. However, that does not mean they *have to* succumb to the temptation. I mentioned in previous chapters that recovery is a way of life that has to be worked at constantly and that it requires some dramatic changes in one's attitude to living. Continued recovery seems to depend on keeping those new attitudes strongly reinforced, in order to prevent some of the old druggy thinking re-emerging. Relapse usually happens after the addict's thinking has been off beam for some time. This is why regular attendance at *Narcotics Anonymous* is essential; the self-help programme of this organisation helps individuals to keep checking out their attitudes to their recovery.

Relapse occurs because addicts have not maintained the disciplines which are necessary to ensure a changed and positive way of life that includes total abstinence. In other words, a relapser has set himself up to use again by not doing everything he needs to do to keep himself drug-free. The following is a list of dangerous behaviour or attitudes that can lead to relapse:

1. *Needing a Convincer*. For some, relapse is an experiment which results from extremely risky thinking. These people may have been in treatment or *Narcotics Anonymous* for some time, but are not 100 per cent convinced that they are addicts; or, they may believe that they are hooked on heroin but believe, wrongly, that they can control the occasional drink or smoke marijuana. Use of any mood-altering chemical can easily lead back to having a fix of heroin. Whether it be from curiosity or thinking they know best, these addicts believe that they have to try just once to find out if they really are addicted or not.

2. *Complacency*. This is usually the main reason for resuming the use of drugs after a lengthy period of abstinence. Believing that the disease has been beaten is extremely dangerous. The development of this attitude usually happens during a very positive period in life – when everything is going well. At these times, it is easy to stop attendance at *Narcotics Anonymous*, cease looking at one's attitudes or behaviour and no longer ask for help. Recovering addicts are probably not thinking about using drugs during these periods but neither are they maintaining the necessary safety requirements. As a result, they let down their guard and may start to believe that because things are going so well, they were never really addicted and that their problem with drugs was just a temporary phase in their lives. Perhaps they could try using drugs in a controlled way now that they have overcome their other problems. They forget the control that heroin had over their lives previously.

3. *Too High Expectations of Self*. Many people set themselves up to fail in recovery because they try to achieve too much, too soon. They try to be perfect in their work situation, in their family relationships, in *Narcotics Anonymous* and often judge themselves as lacking or not coping. As a result, in very black and white terms, they see themselves as failures and become unhappy and full of self-pity. Their negative thinking soon leads them into thinking 'What's the point?' and subsequently justify the need to get stoned.

4. *Unresolved Anger*. Resentments may stem from not being able to forgive people for stuff in the past, or from expecting too much from others in coming to terms with the recovery process. Some recovering addicts can become quite obsessed with what they see as insensitive behaviour of others and see themselves as misunderstood victims. Indeed, this may be the case, but unless they learn to stop trying to control the attitudes of those close to them and let go, the anger is going to fester and eventually erupt. Dangerous thinking like 'I'll show them! I'll use some smack and they'll be sorry!' can be the end result of not dealing appropriately with angry feelings.

5. *Isolation*. Segregating yourself from others can be done in

many ways. Some people isolate themselves because of shyness and fear by completely withdrawing and spending most of their time alone. Others will surround themselves with a large number of acquaintances but never take any risks in getting close to people. As a result, no-one knows them well enough to be of any help. Others still will keep others at bay by being extremely busy all the time. A few will assume an attitude of omnipotence, ignoring suggestions or advice from others. However the isolation is achieved, it is a dangerous situation for recovering addicts. It is a way of avoiding reality, of shunning honest feedback from others. Loneliness can bring misery which, in turn, can encourage the need to obliterate these painful feelings by resuming the use of drugs.

6. *Exhaustion*. Good health and the ability to relax are important for a positive recovery. As they become well and in their efforts to prove themselves, many addicts become high achievers and try to cope with too much. Tiredness may cause the thinking to deteriorate and become negative; this can easily lead to thinking that a little bit of heroin wouldn't make matters any worse.
7. *Involvement with Using Addicts*. Hankering after the old way of life or a genuine desire to help addicted friends too soon in one's own recovery are two reasons for staying involved with those still using. Both these attitudes are hazardous; long-term recovery results from maintaining the new attitudes to living. These beliefs can only be strengthened by being with people who are strong in their recovery. Hanging around drug users brings back druggy thinking and could easily lead to relapse, expecially early in recovery.
8. *Use of Prescribed Mood-altering Chemicals*. On previous occasions I have mentioned the dangers of thinking that it would be acceptable to have the occasional joint. But prescribed drugs like tranquillisers have to be avoided too. Some people may find themselves having to cope with periods of anxiety or depression. The doctor may even prescribe mood-altering chemicals. This is the most subtle way to relapse. ('After all, my doctor said it was O.K.!') Addicts will soon find themselves abusing the tranquillisers by using them in

an uncontrolled way; or more likely, the fact that they have used one mood-altering chemical will lead them right back to taking their favourite drug – heroin. (Please note, there may be physical reasons for prescribing drugs, e.g. during hospital operations. Doctors need to know that the patient is a recovering addict and the drugs should be prescribed in a very controlled way. This does not need to result in relapse. Medical staff at training centres are usually willing to advise if you have any queries about the danger of prescribed medication for addicts.)

THE EFFECTS OF RELAPSE ON AN ADDICTED PERSON

This depends on the individual and the extent of the relapse. Those who have not suffered dramatic consequences will possibly have to return to using yet again and endure more pain. Hopefully, they will learn from their suffering. However, there are others who, after a relatively small use of drugs, will experience such pangs of conscience that they rapidly return to their recovery programme and get well. Many relapsers suffer from loss of pride, self-esteem, coupled with feelings of shame, guilt and remorse. They see themselves as failures; the anger and disappointment of loved ones can endorse this feeling.

HOW CAN RELATIVES AND FRIENDS HELP DEAL WITH RELAPSE?

Remember that relapse does not occur on the spur of the moment. It usually follows a period of unhealthy thinking described above. Obviously, the time to try and prevent relapse is long before those attitudes have become so disturbed as to justify taking that first fix. It is the right of people involved with the addict to advise him when they are feeling uneasy about his behaviour. It is important that the goal for an addict must be total and permanent abstinence from all mood altering chemicals. However, many relapsers have been unfairly dismissed as failures. For someone who has struggled in vain for years, trying to come off drugs, it must be seen as a success if he has achieved one day, one week, one month or one year of sobriety. All too often when someone does relapse we forget these achievements. Do let him know if you are worried about him isolating himself, about him becoming too involved with practising addicts or any of the other behaviour that I described in this chapter. After you have reported your concerns to him you then have to follow the principles of letting go as described in Chapter six. His recovery is his responsibility and you cannot control it for him. If he has decided to use drugs, he will use them, the only way you can help is by accepting your powerlessness over his behaviour.

If your addict does relapse, remember that it is a part of his illness. He has not used drugs again because he was weak-willed, so he does not need to be punished. It is very likely that he is punishing himself enough already. The best way that you can help is to obtain some support for yourself. Use *Families Anonymous;* they will support you in coping with the problems of finding the balance between letting him be responsible for his fight back to recovery, and encouraging him in those attempts. Keep in mind, he is not alone. If he chooses to ask for assistance, *Narcotics Anonymous* will do everything they can to help him recover again. Also, if he has been in treatment, many of the centres mentioned at the end of this book have an after-care or out-patient programme and would be willing to help. If his condition is serious, they may consider re-admitting him for primary treatment.

10. What is Treatment?

Having come to terms with your relative or friend's addiction the next difficult decision to make is where to get some help for him. It can be confusing, and much homework needs to be done because there are many different schools of thought in this country on what is the most effective way to treat an addict. Some believe in encouraging long-term involvement and dependence on therapeutic communities. Others favour viewing addiction as a secondary illness caused by underlying psychological symptoms, and therefore advocate psychiatric help. A number will support the belief that you can never really expect addicts to stay off heroin and that the only way to help them is to control their dependence with a substitute drug like methadone. A large proportion of addicts find their recovery through the self-help group of *Narcotics Anonymous* without professional help. However, some people need help from both professional and self-help organisations in order to achieve a satisfactory rehabilitation.

MINNESOTA EXPERIENCE

Ten years ago, I was one of the cynics who did not believe that addicts got well. At the time I went to the United States to work and study, I had no ambition to pursue a career with addicts. I did however agree to undergo some training in counselling the chemically dependent because I believed I was more liable to be offered a job if I did so. What I saw there really opened my eyes. I saw many young people (who had previously been dismissed as losers) making miraculous recoveries.

The therapeutic school of thought, whose methods I learned, originated in Minnesota in the late 1940's. Over the last thirty years Minnesota has become the state with the most complete, comprehensive and effective system of care ever developed for dealing with chemical dependence. The programme was developed initially to help alcoholics. The success of this model has encouraged a large number of similar organisations to spread through North America and other parts of the world. There are several treatment units in the south of England in the private sector. Nowadays, in such centres, the term alcoholism has broadened to the concept of chemical dependence. It was quickly learned that addiction-prone people are vulnerable to any mood-altering chemicals and must be on guard against all forms of self-medication involving such substances. Many addicts will be dependent on a combination of drugs whether it be heroin and alcohol, alcohol and tranquillisers or any other cocktail of addictive chemicals. Although many alcoholics and addicts (supported by their relatives) will strongly deny the fact – both groups of people have the same illness; only the substance or drug of choice is different.

As a result, centres based on the Minnesota treatment model help all kinds of chemically dependent people, not just heroin addicts. The basic programme for all addicted persons is the same. There are variations in lengths of treatment, depending on the needs of the individual. In England, the average length of stay for a patient involved in this kind of programme is about six to eight weeks. Some individuals may be referred on to halfway houses or extended care programmes if further care is needed.

The aim of this programme is to treat the whole person – physically, psychologically and spiritually. Fundamentally, the philosophy is that recovery from addiction must be based on abstinence from all mood-altering chemicals. There can be no compromising with or deviating from this stance. This treatment model does not spend any time analysing *why* someone becomes an addict. Treatment starts with the facing of the reality of the dependency on drugs and progresses to finding ways of coping with life without them. Addiction is seen as a disease in its own right; no-one is at fault because the illness has developed.

THE RELATIONSHIP WITH A.A. AND N.A.

The original treatment centres based on the Minnesota experience gained a great deal from *Alcoholics Anonymous* and there is still a close relationship between the two organisations although they are quite independent of each other. Subsequently, a similar mutual respect has developed with *Narcotics Anonymous*. In fact, these centres have incorporated the philosophy of A.A. and N.A. into their programmes. The on-going support of these fellowships is very necessary for the patients, as recovery is a process of a lifetime. Also, the spiritual bias of these self-help groups helps change the belief and value systems of the participating addicts. Through this on-going support, patients find a positive and fulfilling way of life.

MULTI – DISCIPLINARY STAFF

As I have stated before, addiction affects so many aspects of an individual's life. Therefore, an effective treatment centre needs staff who specialize in these different areas but who work together as a team. It is not usual for a member of the medical profession to direct the treatment team, although a doctor is an important and integral part of that group. The other members of staff usually include social workers, psychologists, nurses and clergymen, as well as a psychiatric consultant. However, the bulk of the team is often made up of people who are themselves recovering addicts and who have undergone a training in counselling people with this illness. These therapists have the most daily contact with the patients and act as role models for those who still fear that addicts cannot recover from this illness. The treatment staff work as a team, consulting each other as to the best ways to help the patient.

THE THERAPEUTIC COMMUNITY

Each person who is admitted for treatment for addiction is fearful and carrying a great deal of self-hatred. The atmosphere of the treatment centre is therefore supportive and respectful of each individual. The emphasis from the first day is on regarding the patient as a sick individual who wants to get well, rather than a bad person who has to learn how to become good. The community tries to eliminate as much fear as possible.

Every addict has become extremely isolated through his illness. A major step in his recovery is his playing a part in the therapeutic community which exists in the treatment centre. Not only is he expected to be a patient who is participating in his own recovery programme, but he is encouraged to take responsibility for helping his fellow-patient to face his denial system and come to terms with the reality of the illness. Led by the counselling team, the community works together as they support each member of the group through the various stages of the programme. It is amazing how each individual, despite his own denial system, can see quite clearly the delusions and personal defenses of his fellow-patients. Often, people who cannot help themselves can help each other. The mutual caring and support does much to enhance the self-esteem of the individual. Usually, this is the beginning of a spiritual awareness for the patient; a growing belief that the power and support of the group is an essential element in the recovery process. After treatment this is replaced by the fellowship of *Narcotics Anonymous*.

The environment of the community is completely structured and disciplined; the main rule being that patients are expected not to use mood-altering chemicals while undergoing treatment (unless prescribed by the medical staff as part of the detoxification regime). Addicts have had little order in their lives and the programme is built this way to help them adapt to living a more organised way of life.

Importance is also placed on using past and present events as learning experiences. The group helps each individual look at the reality of his drug-using behaviour and helps destroy the delusion that life is wonderful under the influence of heroin or some of its relatives. The major emphasis of the programme is on helping the individual to come to terms with his powerlessness over drugs, an acceptance that if he uses mood-altering chemicals he is no longer in control of his behaviour, the substance is in control of him. He is also encouraged to look at how his using of drugs has damaged himself and caused pain to others.

Recovery also requires learning to relate to other human beings in a respectful, caring way. It is not unusual in a community such as this for relationship problems to occur. An individual may opt out of taking responsibility for therapeutic tasks (like dish washing) by manipulating a newcomer into doing them. Another hurdle may be caused by the forming of cliques, thus preventing other members of the community from establishing constructive communications with others. A variety of techniques can be applied by a patient to stop people from getting to know him, like being aggressive or setting-up another individual to be the focus of the group's attention thereby avoiding the limelight. A withdrawn silence, playing the clown or blaming others for one's own actions are also ways of sidestepping the closeness of others.

In group therapy, each of these situations is an opportunity to look at our own behaviour, to learn how it prevents addicts from recovering and how we can change it. In such a community, recovery is viewed as the individual's responsibility. The group of patients, combined with the counselling staff, act as a mirror, reflecting back the individual's behaviour to himself. Confrontation is a technique that is often used. Done properly, confrontation is non-judgemental; it is a constructive description of how you see an individual's actions, clarifying how they might be harming both himself and his relationships with other people.

Having confronted an individual with a picture of himself, it is necessary for the staff and group to support that patient in coming to the awareness that he has the ability to change. In order to find recovery, addicts have to be prepared to make a commitment to alter whatever self-defeating behaviour needs changing. However, this has to be a long-term goal that only begins in treatment. It takes a long time to adjust to practising a new life-style; this is why supportive aftercare programmes are developed and patients are strongly encouraged to continue attending *Narcotics Anonymous* (and *Alcoholics Anonymous* if they have a problem with alcohol).

THE STRUCTURE OF THE TREATMENT REGIME

As you will have deduced from previous paragraphs, a great emphasis is placed on group therapy in this kind of treatment facility. Most patients are expected to participate in groups from the first day, even when being withdrawn from the effects of drugs under the supervision of the medical team. However, it is anticipated that the participation of those being detoxified will be minimal. These groups are usually led by a trained counsellor but, in addition, patients are often asked to take part in smaller task-orientated groups where a member of staff is not always present. The goal of all groups is to help patients resolve their personal problems with the support of their peer group. Usually the people involved in the smaller groups share similar problems. A typical smaller group might be asked to focus on addiction-related topics such as denial, resentment, grief, assertiveness, or effects of drug addiction on the family.

As well as attending groups, patients are required to listen to lectures usually given by members of the staff team. Such lectures may be about the Twelve Steps of the *Narcotics Anonymous* programme, the physical aspects of drug addiction, how the family is affected, or how to recognize and change certain behaviour or feelings.

On arrival, each patient is assigned to a counsellor. This member of staff is responsible for overseeing the treatment programme of his patients. On average, he will see a patient two or three times a week, encouraging his progress and giving him various recovery-related reading and written assignments to work on. He will also suggest some behavioural changes that the patient could start making. Often, he will encourage his patient to take his problems to the group and ask for help. This is training for using the fellowship of *Narcotics Anonymous* and for not being totally dependent on any one individual. It also encourages openness and honesty in the community. At this time most treatment facilities of this kind are residential. Recently however, some out-patient programmes have been introduced for appropriate patients (see *Directory* for details).

AFTERCARE

The most difficult period in recovery is the first year of abstinence. In fact, recovery only really begins when the patient returns home and learns to live a new sober life-style. Though there are some exceptions, generally, if an addict copes with the stresses of the first twelve months, his recovery will become easier and the threat of relapse is less likely. For this reason, and to support patients working through the problems mentioned in Chapter seven, most models based on the Minnesota method extend primary treatment into what is known as a continuum of care. All those who have completed treatment will be referred on to an aftercare programme. Usually, most of these support systems last for about a year and the frequency of attendance depends on the needs of the individual.

Each person is expected to regularly return to their treatment centre for day counselling. During this time, he will receive group therapy and individual counselling and he may also be expected to attend some lectures. Partners of addicts are also encouraged to be involved so that they can receive some help and support in adjusting to living with a recovering person.

Encouragement to attend *N.A.* meetings, expansion of knowledge and understanding of the Twelve Steps of *Narcotics Anonymous*, improvement of communication skills, are all given on these counselling days as well as an examination of such topics as relapse, assertiveness, rebuilding of self-esteem, relationship or family problems, or looking at ways to cope with day to day living in a more manageable and responsible way.

The aim of the aftercare programme is to provide an opportunity for consolidating and strengthening the more positive way of life that accompanies recovery from drug addiction. Even when the patient has had more than a year's sobriety, the aftercare department is available to those who may be trying to cope with a crisis situation. The attitude is 'we are here if you need us', but, at the same time, gently encouraging less dependence on the treatment centre as time advances and more on the self-help groups, *Narcotics Anonymous* and *Alcoholics Anonymous*.

HALFWAY HOUSES

In the chapter on *Recovery is More Than Just Kicking the Habit* I stressed the need for an addict to be rehabilitated, to learn a new and responsible way of life. I discussed how many addicts in early recovery are only just beginning to learn who they are and what they want. Many, because they started their addiction so young, have no idea of how to live in an organized way. Several need time to grow up emotionally and start catching up with their non-addicted contempories. Others may have no friends and/or relatives who are not addicted and thus need a structured, drug-free environment if they are to maintain their recovery. It may be for all, or several, of these reasons that a patient is referred on to a halfway house.

In the last few years, the need for such establishements has been recognized in this country and slowly they are beginning to appear. (See the *Directory* at the end of the book for further details.) The purpose of these halfway houses is to provide a supportive, but disciplined, environment where residents can start to assume a responsible way of life by finding meaningful employment; at the same time receiving group and individual counselling while continuing recovery and growth.

FAMILY PROGRAMMES

One of the factors that makes this model different from other methods, is the depth of involvement of the relatives and close friends in the treatment programme. Addiction is perceived as a family dis-ease. Therefore everyone in close contact with an addict needs help in coming to terms with the addiction; in learning methods of intervention and becoming aware of what has happened to them as individuals and as a family unit, in living with the illness. Relations are encouraged to believe that they too have the ability to change, if they so wish.

The aims of the family programmes are:

(a) To educate those interested in the disease concept of addiction.

(b) To open up communication within the family network, discussing honestly with the addict the effects of his drug-taking behaviour. The denial system within this group is diminished as a result and the addict is helped in his recovery by facing the reality of the illness.

(c) To help relatives and friends become aware that if they wish to help the addict, they may have to change some of their attitudes and behaviours towards that person.

(d) To encourage involvement in the self-help group of *Families Anonymous* for long-term support.

The extent of involvement of family members depends on the individual treatment centres. Some take an educational role, showing films and giving lectures on visitor's day; others have family groups meeting once a week where relatives of different patients meet to discuss common problems; still more have individual families meeting with the patient's counsellor; a few present specialized weekends, while yet others organize long-term treatment for family members. Most treatment centres offer a combination of two or three of these facilities.

It is my particular bias, but I do strongly believe that, inevitably whatever support is offered to the families of addicts is not enough. In this country, we deny the extent of our heroin problem. So little help is provided to help those who have become slaves to the drug. Even less is offered to the many relatives and friends who have suffered a great deal of anguish and torment.

I hope that in sharing my experience, I have given some encouragement and practical suggestions that can help both you—and your addict—recover from addiction to heroin.

How to recognise heroin addiction

There are ways you can tell if a member of your family or a friend is using heroin. Some of the following indicators might lead you to suspect addiction:

1. **Changes in personality**: aggressive behaviour that swings to charming people-pleasing; secretiveness, withdrawal from family life, disinterest in others, lying, stealing, manipulating to get money, loss of concentration.

2. **Physical appearance**: losing weight, diminishing appetite, fragile look, not caring about appearance, sleepiness with occasional snapping awake, perspiring face, shaking hands and sniffing nose in withdrawal, wearing long sleeves to cover trackmarks, avoiding eye contact, tiny pupils when high, enormous when withdrawing, pallor or pale complexion.

3. **Sense of time**: Staying in bed all or most of the day, staying out late, or all of the night, avoiding usual family rituals like meals and so on.

4. **Suspicious objects**: Lemons used for dissolving heroin powder before injecting, silver foil burnt on one side used to 'chase the dragon', envelopes containing drugs, hypodermic syringes and needles.

Author's Note: Unfortunately, because of the scepticism and suspicion about self-help groups, *Narcotics Anonymous* has been dismissed by some people as a "bunch of crazies". These critics have failed to recognise that this organization has been around for a long time (since 1953) in the United States. It has been modelled on the even longer-lasting, and just as successful *Fellowship* *of Alcoholics Anonymous*. The main difference between the two organizations is that membership of *N.A.* requests an honest desire to abstain from all mood changing chemicals – not just alcohol.

Glossary of Terms

One of the greatest hindrances to helping an addict is the feeling of ignorance and impotence that the layman experiences. Very often this happens because the drug world is surrounded by mystique. It has a culture of its own which is created by an air of secretiveness, self-protection, and language.

Another area of confusion is the jargon used by recovering addicts. Many relatives and friends can feel left out because of the use of jargon.

ADDICT. *See* DRUG ADDICT.

ADDICTIVE DRUG. A substance that is likely to be the focus, physically and psychologically, of chemical dependency. *See* CHEMICAL DEPENDENT, CHEMICAL DEPENDENCY, DRUG ADDICT.

AFTER-CARE. The programme of care supplied by most treatment centres to support patients in the early stages of recovery, after completing the primary treatment programme.

AL-ANON. The sister organization to *Alcoholics Anonymous*. A self-help group for the friends and relatives of alcoholics.

ALCOHOLIC. One who is dependent on alcohol, one who, when he drinks cannot predict what the outcome will be as the alcohol controls his attitudes, feelings and behaviour. Medical resources estimate conservatively that some 200,000 men and women in the United Kingdom suffer from alcoholism.

ALCOHOLICS ANONYMOUS (AA). A worldwide network of self-help groups started in the US for those suffering from the disease of alcoholism. To date its programme has proved the most succesful way of helping alcoholics to recover. The only qualification for membership is to have an honest desire to give up drinking alcohol.

ALCOHOLISM. A progressive, terminal illness suffered by the alcoholic.

AMPHETAMINE. A group of stimulant drugs. *See* UPPERS.

AMPS. Ampoules or glass phials usually containing Methadone.

ANOREXIA. An illness from which some young female addicts suffer. The sufferer is repulsed by her own body fat and obsessively refuses to eat. Many of the young people with this illness also find benefit from attending the self-help group *Anorexics Aid*.

BARBS. *See* BARBITURATE.

BARBITURATE. A widely prescribed group of drugs used as sleeping pills.

BENZODIAZEPINE. A generic term for tranquilisers such as Librium, Valium, Ativan, and so on.

BILLY WHIZZ. *See* AMPHETAMINE.

BLACK BOMBER. Capsules of Durophet (black), a brand of amphetamine. *See* UPPERS.

BLACKOUT. A period of amnesia usually resulting from excessive drinking of alcohol.

BLOW. *See* MARIJUANA.

BLUES. Drinamyl (blue tablets), an amphetamine, previously known as *Purple Hearts*.

BUST. Police raid or interference.

CANNABIS. The botanical name for marijuana.

CHARLIE. *See* COCAINE.

CHASING [THE] DRAGON. Inhalation of heroin, which is placed on silver foil and heated from underneath. The vaporized fumes are inhaled through a funnel made of paper or an old pen.

CHEMICAL DEPENDENCY. Addiction to any mood-altering chemical, including alcohol and all drugs.

CHEMICALLY DEPENDENT. A general term describing all those who are addicted to any mood-altering chemical, whether it be alcohol, tranquilisers or street drugs.

CHINESE. Non-National Health heroin that is usually a yellow powder. So called because the first supplies came from the Far East.

CLEAN. To be off drugs.

COCAINE. Made from the Coca plant in South America, a white

crystalline powder that is a powerful stimulant, often wrongly thought to be non-addictive. *See* UPPER.

CODEINE. Widely available alkaloid of Opium. In desperation used as heroin substitute. *See* OPIATE.

COKE. *See* COCAINE.

COLD TURKEY. Sudden withdrawal from drugs without medical detoxification or supervision.

CONFRONT. To describe to a person his behaviour and body language in a constructive and caring way, with the purpose of helping him look at how he might change his behaviour and attitudes.

CONTROLLING. Dominating or manipulating other people's thoughts and actions to one's own benefit (playing God).

DEALER. A drug supplier.

DETOX. *See* DETOXIFICATION.

DETOXIFICATION. A treatment regime of a diminishing course of drugs, to help safely withdraw an addict from use of alcohol or drugs. *See* HEMINEVRIN and METHADONE.

DEXEDRINE. Yellow tablets. *See* AMPHETAMINE.

DEXIES. *See* DEXEDRINE.

DICONAL. Pink tablets, often crushed and injected. *See* NARCOTIC.

DISEASE. A disorder in, or want of health in mind or body; an ailment or cause of pain; an illness.

DOWNER. *See* BARBITURATE.

DRUG ADDICT. One who is dependent on addictive drugs whether they are prescribed or bought off the street. The drugs control his feelings, thoughts and behaviour.

DRUG ADDICTION. A terminal illness caused by dependence on addictive drugs.

ENABLING. The protective behaviour of those close to an addict, when they take over responsibility for the addict's acts, thus cushioning him from the reality of his illness and hindering his recovery.

FAMILIES ANONYMOUS (FA). The sister organization to *Narcotics Anonymous*, a self-help group for the friends and relatives of addicts.

FAMILY ILLNESS. Addiction is often described as a family illness: although no one is to blame for the addiction, those involved with the addict also contribute to the progression of the addiction by being overly protective. Many of those involved also suffer greatly both as individuals and as family units, as a result of living in close proximity to the addiction.

FAMILY PROGRAMME. Many treatment centres offer a programme of recovery for the family illness for relatives of addicts.

FEEDBACK. An honest but constructive opinion of another's behaviour.

FELLOWSHIP. The support and companionship of any *Twelve Step* recovery programme, be it AA, NA, Al-Anon, or FA.

FIX. To inject into the vein.

FLASHBACK. Brief return to a bad trip. *See* HALLUCINOGENS.

FREE BASING. Dissolving impure cocaine in ammonia or sodium bicarbonate. The cocaine sinks to the bottom and can be later smoked in a water pipe.

GANGA. *See* MARIJUANA.

GEAR. *See* HEROIN.

GOOF BALLS. Barbiturate capsules.

GOUCHING OUT. When large quantities of heroin are taken, the user gets sleepy, his eyes close, his head nods and it is a struggle to remain conscious.

GRASS. *See* MARIJUANA.

H *See* HEROIN.

HABIT. To have one is to be addicted.

HALFWAY HOUSE. A centre for those who need additional support after completing treatment, where they are encouraged to start to become part of the outside community through jobs and social lives, whilst still being involved in group and individual counselling.

HALLUCINOGENS. Any drug, such as LSD or mescalin, that induces hallucinations. *See* TRIPPING, FLASHBACK.

HARD DRUGS. Generally that group of drugs listed under the *Controlled Drugs Regulations*, including the opiates and other true narcotics, cocaine and the amphetamines.

HASH. The resinous extract of the dried flower tops of the female marijuana plant. A dark brown or black cake.

HEMINEVRIN. Yellow, rubgy-football shaped, gelatin capsules. A sedative widely prescribed to ease the pain of withdrawal from alcohol.

HENRY. *See* HEROIN.

HEPATITIS. Inflammation of the liver, often caused in addicts by the use of unsterile needles.

HERB. *See* MARIJUANA.

HEROIN. White or brown powder synthesized from morphine, obtained from the opium poppy.

HIGH. Drug induced euphoria or elation.

HIGHBALL. A mixture of heroin with either cocaine or amphetamine.

HIGHER POWER. God, or something outside ourselves in which we can have faith. For many recovering addicts, the NA programme itself is their higher power.

HOOKED. Addicted.

HORSE. *See* HEROIN.

JACK UP. To inject a drug.

JOINT. A hand-made cigarette of tobacco and either hash or marijuana.

JUNKIE. Heroin addict.

KICK THE HABIT. To stop using drugs. *See* COLD TURKEY, WITHDRAWAL.

LIBRIUM. Green and yellow or green and black capsules, blue and green tablets or ampoules of powder. *See* MINOR TRANQUILISERS.

MAINLINING. Injecting into the vein and not the muscle.

MAJOR TRANQUILISERS. Non-addictive antipsychotic agents used in the treatment of serious psychiatric disorders.

MANDIES. *See* MANDRAX.

MANDRAX. White tablets with Mx marked on them. Methaqualone, a sleeping pill.

MANIPULATION. *See* CONTROLLING.

MARIJUANA. The best known of the soft drugs, known as Cannabis Sativa botanically, taken by smoking the dried leaves.

METHADONE. White tablets, ampoules of clear liquid, or an orange-yellow linctus. A synthetic substitute for heroin.

MINOR TRANQUILISERS. Called the anxiolytics because they allay anxiety. The largest group, the benzodiazepines (valium, librium, tranxene, evacalm, etc.), are extremely widely prescribed and are by no means 'minor' in their long term effects.

MORPHINE. White or brown powder or ampoules of clear liquid. *See* OPIATE.

NARCOTIC. Highly addictive, potent, pain-killing drug. A so-called hard drug.

NARCOTICS ANONYMOUS. A self-help group based on the *Twelve Step* programme of *Alcoholics Anonymous*, but developed to help those who are dependent on any addictive drug, including alcohol.

NEMBIES. *See*. NEMBUTAL.

NEMBUTAL. Yellow capsules of pentobarbitone. *See* BARBITURATE.

OPIATE. Drugs derived from opium, though synthetics like methadone are also sometimes described as Opiates.

OPIUM. In its raw state, a dark brown sticky substance obtained by 'milking' the unripe seed heads of the opium poppy, Papaver Somniferum.

PETHIDINE. White tablets or ampoules of clear liquid. *See* NARCOTIC.

PEOPLE PLEASING. Trying to please others at one's own expense; being non-assertive.

PHYSEPTONE. Proprietary name for methadone.

PILL POPPER. One who uses drugs in pill form, usually barbiturates, amphetamines and tranquilisers.

PINNED. Having pinhead-sized pupils in the eye, a sure sign of heroin consumption.

POLYDRUG USER. One who abuses a variety of drugs.

POPPING. Injecting a drug into the skin or muscle, not the vein.

POT. *See* MARIJUANA.

POTHEAD. One who smokes marijuana.

POWERLESSNESS. The inability to control mood-altering chemicals. Also used by FA to mean the inability to control other people.

PRIMARY TREATMENT. Initial treatment of an addict involving detoxification, group therapy, individual counselling, and the involvement of the family to help start the recovery process. Usually lasts from six to eight weeks in the UK.

PROGRAMME. A course of treatment or recovery.

REALITY THERAPY. A form of psychotherapy that helps the addict to look at how he can take responsibility for changing his attitudes, behaviour and feelings at the present time, so becoming able to love and be loved and to feel worthwhile. It is thought more important for the addict to accept that he *is* an addict than to try and find out why he is.

RECOVERY. The gradual process of becoming well from the illness of drug addiction, which involves both physical withdrawal from drugs and mental rehabilitation.

RED DEVILS. *See* SECONAL.

REEFER. *See* JOINT.

REHABILITATION. Learning a new and responsible way of life.

RELAPSE. The resumption of the use of mood-altering chemicals.

RUSH. A wave of drug-induced euphoria.

SCORE. To obtain drugs.

SCRIPT. A prescription for drugs.

SECONAL. Orange and red capsules. *See* BARBITURATE.

SEDATIVISM. Dependence on any sedative, whether it be alcohol or drugs. *See* DOWNERS.

SHIT. *See* MARIJUANA.

SMACK. *See* HEROIN.

SNORT. To inhale a powder into the nose through a paper tube (often a rolled banknote) so the drug can reach the blood through the nasal membrane. The usual method for taking cocaine.

SNOW. *See* COCAINE.

SOFT DRUGS. A now discredited distinction, since it is realized that no mood-altering chemicals are safe as the word 'soft' implies. Usually taken to be marijuana, barbiturates and tranquilisers.

SONERYL. Pink tablets. *See* BARBITURATE.

SPACED [OUT]. *See* HIGH.

SPEED. See AMPHETAMINE.

SPEEDBALL. A mixture of amphetamine and heroin. *See* HIGHBALL.

SPEEDFREAK. One who takes amphetamine, usually addictively.

SPIKE. A syringe needle.

STASH. A hidden supply of drugs or the hiding place.

STONED. *See* HIGH.

STRAIGHT. To be clean, or a person who has never taken drugs. *See* CLEAN.

SULPH. Amphetamine Sulphate, a white powder injected in solution.

TEAHEAD. *See* POTHEAD.

TOOT. *See* SNORT

TOUGH LOVE. Helping an addict to face reality while still caring.

TRACK MARKS or TRACKS. Scars left by frequent injection in the same veins.

TRANKS. *See* MINOR TRANQUILISERS.

TREATMENT. *See* PRIMARY TREATMENT.

TRIPPING. To be under the influence of an hallucinogen. *See* LSD.

TUIES. *See* TUINAL.

TUINAL. An orange and blue capsule. *See* BARBITURATE.

TURKEY. *See* COLD TURKEY.

TWELVE STEPS. The basis of the recovery programme of AA, Al-Anon, NA and FA.

UNMANAGEABLE. The quality of chaos in an addict's life both while he is still using and when in early recovery.

UPPER. *See* STIMULANT.

VALIUM. Pink syrup, white, yellow or blue tablets, or ampoules. *See* MINOR TRANQUILISERS.

VALS. *See* VALIUM.

WEED *See* MARIJUANA.

WHIZZ. *See* BILLY WHIZZ.

WITHDRAWAL. The process of coming off drugs, often accompanied by sweating, cramps, depression and aching limbs. *See* COLD TURKEY.

WORKS. A syringe and needle, or any apparatus serving as such.

YELLOW PERIL. *See* HEPATITIS.

Dictionary of Helping Agencies

Self-Help Groups

Alcoholics Anonymous (for those with a problem with Alcohol).

A.A. General Services, P.O. Box 514, 11 Redcliffe Gardens, London SW10 9BQ. Tel. 01 352 9779.

Families Anonymous, 88 Caledonian Road, London N1 9DN. Tel. 01 278 8805

Narcotics Anonymous, P.O. Box 246, London SW10. Tel. 01 351 0794.

The above are National Headquarter numbers. They will be able to tell you where your local meetings are.

Residential In-patient Programmes

Broadreach House, 465 Tavistock Road, Plymouth PL6 7HE.
Contact person: Treatment Co-ordinator. Tel. 0752 790 000.

Broadway Lodge, Oldmixon Road, Weston-super-Mare, Avon, BS24 9NN.
Contact person: Head of Treatment, Tel. 0934 812319.

Charter Clinic, (Chelsea),
P.O. Box 23, 1–5 Radnor Walk, London SW3 4PB.
Contact person: Bruce Lloyd. Tel 01 351 1272

Charter Clinic (Hampstead),
P.O. Box 119, 11 Fellows Road, Hampstead, London NW3 3LA.
Contact Person: Bruce Lloyd. Tel. 01 586 8062.

Clouds House (Life Anew Trust),
East Knoyle, Nr. Salisbury, Wiltshire SP3 6BE.
Contact person: The Director (Peter McCann). Tel. 0747 83650.

Farm Place, Ockley, Surrey, RH5 5NG.
Contact persons: Jim or Joyce Ditzler. Tel 030679 742.

Out-patient Treatment

Alcohol/Drugs Advice Centre, 75 Uplands Cresent, Uplands, Swansea SA2 0EX, Glam.
Contact person: Alan Douglas. Tel 0792 472519

Chemical Dependency Centre, c/o St. Mary Abbotts Hospital, Block B, 3rd Floor, Marloes Road, London W8 5LQ.
Contact persons: Tristan Millington-Drake or Eileen Furgerson Tel. 01 938 2982

5 Eaton House, 39 Upper Grosvenor Street, London W1X 9PA.
Contact person: Jim or Joyce Ditzler. Tel 01 491 8409.

Southern Addiction Treatment Services, 49 High Street, Haslemere, Surrey.
Contact person: Dr. Diana Samways. Tel 0428 3021.

Weston Counselling Services, Lloyds Bank Chambers, 14 Walliscote Road, Weston-super-Mare, Avon, BS23 1UQ.
Contact person: Eric Evans or Alan Laine. Tel. 0934 415711.

Halfway Houses

Larkhill House, 63 Devonshire Road, Weston-super-Mare, Avon.
Patients: Male, 12 bed unit.
Contact persons: Alan Davies, Pauline or Eric Evans. Tel 0934 25971.

Kintyre, 1 Newtons Road, Weston-super-Mare, Avon.
Patients: Female, 12 bed Unit.
Contact persons; Judy Hardin, Pauline or Eric Evans.
Tel. 0934 20341.